Television and Me

The Memoirs of John Logie Baird

Television and Me

The Memoirs of John Logie Baird

Edited by

Malcolm Baird

It is the beginnings of invented *things which appeal to me. For it is at their beginnings that we may detect their true natures, and feel the impact of Man's imagination which created them.*

Lance Sieveking

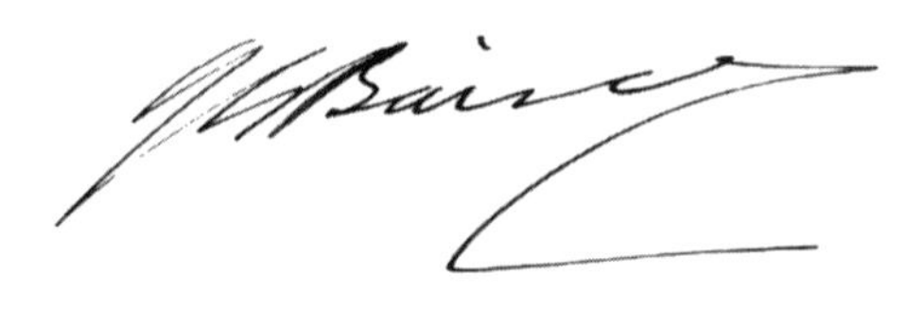

mercatpress
www.mercatpress.com

First published as *Sermons, Soap and Television* in 1988 by the Royal Television Society
Second edition published in 1990
This revised and expanded edition published in 2004 by Mercat Press Ltd., 10 Coates Crescent, Edinburgh EH3 7AL
www.mercatpress.com
Reprinted in 2004

ISBN: 184183 0631

Set in Rockwell and Perpetua at Mercat Press

Printed and bound in Great Britain by Bell & Bain Ltd

Contents

Illustrations

Preface

by Malcolm Baird

Television became a reality in January 1926 when John Logie Baird demonstrated the world's first television pictures. The images were sent from one side of a room to the other, mechanically scanned as 30 vertical strips of light which showed a head-and-shoulders picture of the person being televised. After a few years the development of electronic scanning and the cathode ray tube led to much higher resolution, but Baird's television system was the world's first and it stimulated research by the big radio conglomerates in Britain and the U.S.A. The very simplicity of the signals allowed them to be transmitted through normal telephone lines, or on medium or short radio wavelengths. Soon the range of transmission was vastly increased; television was sent from London to Glasgow in 1927 and from London to New York in 1928. The system could be modified to show colour or three-dimensional pictures; the use of infra-red rays instead of light enabled a person in total darkness to be televised. All this was achieved before 1930.

In order to show television to a mass audience in Britain, Baird's company needed the cooperation of the B.B.C. which held the monopoly on public broadcasting. Its Director General, Sir John Reith, disliked television; late in his life he said that he had been 'frightened of it from the start'. After long negotiations, on 30 September 1929 Baird Television Ltd. began to broadcast its programmes on an experimental basis using B.B.C. medium wave facilities, after radio broadcasting had stopped at 11 p.m. At first, only one transmitter was available and the vision and sound signals had to be sent alternately, but after March 1930 two transmitters were used, enabling vision and sound to be sent simultaneously.

From 1930 onwards, electronic television technology gradually advanced as an alternative to mechanical methods, and Baird's company had to adapt to the change. At first, cash flow was limited and Baird had only a small research staff. New capital became available in 1932 when Baird Television Ltd. was taken over by a cinema conglomerate, the Gaumont British Picture Corporation. This enabled Baird Television Ltd. to expand its research programme on electronic television as well as improvement of the mechanical techniques.

However, in the summer of 1933, Baird himself was deprived of executive power; this boardroom coup was kept from public notice as he retained the nominal title of managing director. Thereafter he spent most of his time doing research on large-screen television at his private laboratory in Sydenham, near the Crystal Palace. In early 1937 another blow to his pride came when the B.B.C. adopted the Marconi-EMI-R.C.A. electronic system of television in preference to Baird Television Ltd.'s system, which at that time was a hybrid using both mechanical and electronic techniques.

Despite this setback, Baird Television Ltd. continued to operate successfully, making receivers and developing television for cinemas; Baird still received an ample salary. This all ended in September 1939 when war broke out and television broadcasting was stopped. The company promptly went into receivership and Baird became, in his own words, 'a free agent'. His first action was to move his family to the safety of Bude, in north Cornwall. He chose to carry on with research at the Sydenham laboratory at his own expense, but he came down to stay with us in Bude every few weeks. He would arrive tired and preoccupied, but he quickly settled down to a few days of relaxation. He would take my sister Diana and me for slow walks along the beach, or show us simple optical experiments with a lens or a prism.

His wartime research was on high-definition electronic colour television and stereoscopic television. The results were spectacular, but they attracted little attention because of the war. Difficult working conditions took their toll on Baird's health and in May 1941 he entered Tempsford Hall, a health farm in Bedfordshire, as a patient. Soon after entering the hall he had a heart attack and he remained there for 4 months, isolated from his laboratory and undergoing a strict diet. During his stay he lost 20 kg and had to have his suit altered by the local tailor.

A fellow patient, the distinguished lawyer Philip Morrell, suggested that Baird should while away the time by writing his memoirs. This idea had already been at the back of his mind and he seized upon it. A shorthand secretary was summoned, and for a few hours every day he dictated. He had no means of checking names and dates; everything had to come from his memory and he was undergoing a near-starvation diet. It comes as no surprise that the memoirs contain the occasional mistake; often the continuity is broken while he tells a funny story or makes personal remarks about someone or talks about his experiences with spiritualism, which was one of his minor interests. Most of the memoirs have a detached tone with a touch of dry humour, but sometimes Baird breaks into fury, as when he describes his working conditions as an apprentice in Glasgow factories. Everything was dutifully taken down by the secretary. The memoirs were typed up in double spacing on foolscap sheets as chapters I to IX, amounting to 45,000 words, covering his life up to 1941.

Soon after his discharge from Tempsford Hall, Baird embarked upon a new project on high-speed signalling, sponsored by Cable and Wireless Ltd. This provided some badly-needed financial support, while he also continued his work on colour and stereoscopic television. By the end of the war he was worn out. He had a stroke in February 1946, made a partial recovery, but then died in his sleep on 14 June 1946.

His death hit the family hard, emotionally and financially. Since January 1945 we had been living at Bexhill, but in the spring of 1947 we moved north to the old family home in Helensburgh, 'The Lodge', where my aunt Annie Baird made us welcome. Diana and I went to school in Helensburgh but my mother had fallen into a state of clinical depression and spent some time undergoing hospital treatment. Her recovery was completed by her return to the sunshine of South Africa where she had been born (in 1907) and raised. Between 1959 and 1986 she resumed her musical career, teaching pianoforte and giving the occasional public recital under her maiden name Margaret Albu.

13 August 1988 marked the centennial of John Logie Baird's birth and there were several public events recognising his contributions. In Helensburgh, the West Parish Church held a service of dedication of memorial stained glass windows; the B.B.C. broadcast a docudrama on Baird and his life; and my mother, by now living in Scotland, was invited to appear on Terry Wogan's chat show. Last but not least, the Royal Television Society, with financial help from the B.B.C., brought out a first edition of Baird's memoirs under the title of *Sermons, Soap and Television*. Through an oversight this differed slightly from the title originally intended by Baird: *Sermons, Socks and Television*. The book was edited by Tom Singleton from a carbon copy of the 1941 memoirs which my mother had passed on to me. The family was profoundly grateful to the R.T.S. for publishing the memoirs after almost half a century.

In the autumn of 1999 I was approaching retirement from my post as a provincial professor of chemical engineering in Canada. At last I had some spare time and I entered into a collaboration with the Scottish-based historical writer Antony Kamm to produce a definitive biography of my father. One of our aims was to clarify various legends that had grown up around him and his life, by referring to as many original sources as we could find. The project took nearly three years and resulted in a 450-page volume, *John Logie Baird: A Life*, published in July 2002 by the National Museum of Scotland. The book was the basis of a 75-minute television documentary entitled 'JLB—The Man Who Saw the Future' first aired on B.B.C. 4 in January 2003.

Just before our book went to press, an unexpected event occurred. The Hastings Museum and Art Gallery acquired a package of papers and photographs including two revised and annotated drafts of my father's memoirs which had lain for years in the office of his lawyer, K.E. Shelley, Q.C. Antony Kamm and I closely studied these revised drafts and included a brief textual history in an Appendix added to our book just before the publication deadline. Some of the annotations were in Baird's handwriting and some were in Margaret Baird's handwriting. Editorial comments had been added in another hand, which may have been that of James Spence, a journalist friend of Baird. It seems that after 1941, efforts had been made by my parents and Spence to bring the memoirs to a more polished state, but Spence died suddenly in April 1944 and the papers were deposited with Mr. Shelley.

In the same package at the Hastings Museum there is an additional posthumous chapter of the memoirs, written by my mother in 1948 under the heading 'Chapter X'. This short chapter is handwritten with many deletions and changes and my mother had presumably sent it to Shelley who placed it with the earlier typed chapters. Thereafter she never mentioned Chapter X to the family and she died in 1996.

The discovery of my mother's chapter and the revised versions of chapters I to IX has provided the impetus for publication of this new edition of the memoirs. They add a pithy and readable account to the several detailed books on Baird which have recently appeared, and are listed under 'Further Reading' after Chapter X.

As I noted earlier, the memoirs contain a few errors on dates. Baird also had a tendency to misname people or organisations he disliked. The memoirs are sprinkled with quotations from classical authors (Goethe, Dante, Matthew Arnold) but, alas, a few slight errors are to be found there as well. I have taken the liberty of adding footnotes to correct points of detail and provide additional historical background.

Pictures have been chosen to relate as far as possible to the text of the memoirs. About half of the pictures are from the Baird family collection, going back as early as 1890. In addition, I wish to thank the following organisations which have kindly given permission to use their pictures, and their staff who have been unfailingly helpful; the Alexandra Palace Television Society (Simon Vaughan), the B.B.C. (Jacquie Kavanagh), the Daily Mail and Atlantic Syndication (Rebecca Barnard), the Hastings Museum and Art Gallery (Victoria Williams), the National Museum of Photography, Film and Television (John Trenouth), the National Museum of Scotland (Lesley Taylor) and the Royal Television Society (Clare Colvin). Paul Sieveking has kindly consented to the use of a quotation by his father on the title page. Other individuals who have been of great help are Robert Britton, Donald McLean, and Richard West. Every effort has been made to trace other possible copyright holders and obtain permission from them; where this has not proved possible, omissions can be rectified in subsequent editions of this book. I am especially indebted to Antony Kamm for his general encouragement and advice on this project, and to Ray Herbert, a former employee of Baird Television Ltd., for many helpful discussions.

In closing my preface, I should remind readers that the memoirs were written a long time ago. The author L.P. Hartley has wisely observed that 'the past is a different country; they do things differently there.' A century has passed since my father, as a teenager, was inspired by the writings of H.G. Wells and the late Victorian enthusiasm for science and technology. Like Wells, he was frustrated and infuriated by the British class system which he likened to the Indian caste system. Later on, his chief bugbear was the B.B.C., which was a prim and high-minded monopoly, much in contrast to its present state. Television technology itself has changed too; today's systems are so complex that the public simply takes them for granted, but in the early days of television there was a sense of wonder and even non-technical people were interested in the electrical and mechanical details. This attitude is epitomized by the quote from Lance Sieveking on the title page. Against this historical background, *Television and Me* gives us a vivid and frank account of John Logie Baird, his struggles and his achievements.

Hamilton, Canada
February 2004

Chapter One

I was born in 1888. My father was the Minister of the West Parish of Helensburgh, a small watering place near Glasgow. He had gone there immediately after finishing his studies at Glasgow University, where he obtained his M.A. and B.D. and showed remarkable talent. A small body of residents in this little seaside resort sent a request to the University that a student should be sent to open a small church to serve their needs, and my father was chosen for the task.

Among those who came to his church was Miss Jessie Inglis, one of a wealthy family of shipbuilders, who came to Helensburgh for the summer, and looked rather askance at the struggling young clergyman when he proposed marriage. The opposition, however, was overcome, and Miss Jessie Inglis became Mrs. Baird. The little church prospered; my father must have been energetic and enterprising. Among his other activities he formed a literary society, of which the future Prime Minister, Bonar Law, was once a member.

All this, however, was before I was born, and by the time I became old enough to notice what was going on around me, the excitement and initial effort were over. The congregation was firmly established and had built for itself a substantial grey stone church with an impressive steeple.[1] The congregation of the rival Episcopalian church had run out of funds before being able to complete the building, so that their church remained steepleless.

I was, I am told, a healthy and energetic infant until, at the age of two, I contracted a very serious illness—stoppage of the bowels was the name given to it—and I was ill for several months, and remained for a time a delicate weakling. However, I remember little of all this except for a faint image of myself under an apple tree on a red blanket, the first impression to remain in my mind, and now nearly fifty years old.

In those days life moved far more slowly and with much more dignity than it does today. There were no motor cars, no wireless sets, no aeroplanes; the

1 The new church was officially the West Established Church; it became known as St Bride's Church. The building was demolished in 1992 and the site is now occupied by the Helensburgh Library. The memorial stained glass window for Rev. John Baird (d.1932) was among several windows recovered before the demolition, and restored. It can now be seen in the library.

Portrait of John Logie Baird as a baby in 1890, when he was still 'a healthy and energetic infant', before his serious illness.

Baird in 1908 at the controls of his Humber Olympic tri-car which he later described as 'a perfect scrap heap on wheels'. The passenger is believed to be his cousin, Jeanie Coates.

telephone was a novelty possessed by a few of the more wealthy; the gramophone, a strange instrument, appeared occasionally in booths at fairs held in the village. Mysterious cylinders revolved beneath a great glass dome; those who paid twopence had the privilege of inserting rubber tubes into their ears and hearing a squeaking voice proclaiming some dissertation.

I remember seeing a motor car for the first time. I must have been about eight years old. It was a strange affair, with immense wooden wheels. Ten years later I bought a second-hand motor cycle, with a tiny engine under the seat. It had been, in its day, the last word in cycles, and was called a 'Kellycomb Antoinette'; it cost me five pounds. After a little while I sold it, and became the possessor of a nondescript tri-car,[2] a perfect scrap heap on wheels, which was known locally as 'young Baird's reaper and binder', from the appalling noise it made.

In our social life the old caste system, though already in a precarious condition, still survived. In the lowest caste were the beggars, tramps and gypsies, analogous to 'The Untouchables'; then came the dustmen, labourers and navvies, and next but quite a distance removed, the smaller tradesmen such as butchers, bakers and grocers. These again merged into the small businessman, and the businessman in turn expanded to the city magnate. Mixing into this stratum and oscillating between its extremes were the professional men, doctors, lawyers and clergy. At the top of the tree, a race apart, were the country gentlemen, the idle land owners of the County, engaged in 'shootin', huntin'and fishin'' and right at the very top of the tree was the laird or chief, Sir lain Colquhoun of Luss.

Helensburgh received its very unfortunate name from Lady Helen Colquhoun, wife of Sir James Colquhoun, who founded the town.[3] The Colquhouns in my day still dominated Helensburgh, and the name Colquhoun was a common one in the district.

I had a rather strange experience in this connection in New York. A little solicitor called Coen told me that his ancestors came from my part of the country and that his name Coen was, in fact, a corruption of Colquhoun. This may be so, although it sounded farfetched.

This is an example of the very flattering esteem in which the Scottish race is held, particularly by the Jews, whose eagerness to establish a Scottish ancestry seems rather peculiar when one considers that the Jews are members

2 The tri-car was a Humber Olympic, manufactured in 1904 and rated at a top speed of 17½ miles per hour.* [The asterisk against some of these footnotes signifies that the information is from *John Logie Baird: A Life* by Antony Kamm and Malcolm Baird.]

3 Helensburgh received its charter in 1802 and its full history is given in the book *200 Years of Helensburgh*, edited by Stewart Noble and Kenneth Crawford (Argyll Publishing, 2002).

of a civilisation whose traditions and teachings have dominated a great part of the civilised world. The Jews were a learned and highly civilized people at a time when the Scots were wild barbarians.

I never saw Sir lain Colquhoun, but he had a great reputation as a sportsman and an upholder of the old country clan traditions. I was impressed by a picture of him which appeared continually in the society papers, showing him a fine figure of a man in highland costume, with short kilt, bare legs and bare feet, striding vigorously over his native heather, oblivious of thistles and cow pats, but not of press photographers.

The house in which we lived was not a manse but belonged to my father, who had purchased it after his marriage with the assistance of my mother's dowry. It was an old stone house called 'The Lodge'[4] built in the most inconvenient possible fashion, but with a fair sized garden, in which I spent the greatest part of my childhood, playing with Willie Brown, the small son of the gardener who lived next door. The gardener was known as 'Auld Broon', and was one of the assistant gardeners to Ure of Cairn Dhu, a local magnate. He was paid one pound a week, and on this supported a wife and two children in happy contentment. They had a room and an attic, for which he paid five shillings a week rent, and was able to buy all necessities and even save something out of the remaining fifteen shillings, although Willie had a little sister who also had to be supported. Willie had only one ambition; to be a gardener like his father. A happy, healthy boy, he became in turn a happy healthy young gardener, untroubled by any hopeless ambition to be one of the gentry.

The latter, clergymen, doctors, the county and most of the businessmen, he regarded with complete contempt. Modern education would have wrecked poor Willie's happiness; he would have learned to despise gardeners; he would have been taught that he could have become one of the gentry, and even, by great effort on his part, risen to be Prime Minister; he would have been haunted and tormented by discontent and frustration. My father's church knew better, the flock were taught 'be content with such things as ye have,' 'blessed are the humble' and other such useful maxims. The Sunday School children's favourite hymn was:

'Day by day the little daisy
Looks up with its yellow eye;
Never longing, never wishing.
It were hanging up on high'.

4 'The Lodge' was built in about 1870. Mr Baird had bought it from a Mrs Jane Allen in November 1880 for £1100. At that time it was a bungalow; the second storey was added a few years later.

I was a very imaginative child and retain a memory of an episode which haunted me although it was probably quite meaningless. One Sunday morning when I was a very small boy, I was left at home when the family went to church. I was standing at the window with my head just reaching the window-ledge and the house was very quiet. Suddenly an aged man, bent over his stick, tottered round the corner of the house and looked up at me. I was terrified and jumped back from the window in horror. A strange idea took root in my mind that the old man was myself grown old and the horror that I should one day become such a creature made me turn and run from the window.

Who the old man was I do not know, probably some visitor wandering round the large garden as they sometimes did, or was it some child's day-dreaming vision? Sometimes I wonder if one day revisiting the old home, I will look up and see looking from the dining-room window a horrified little boy.

Willie and I were inseparable; from morning to night we played in the large garden, building mud houses. I had two elder sisters, Annie and Jean, and an elder brother James, but Willie filled the horizon until I was five years old, when I was taken to school. My first school was an extraordinary Dickensian menage, kept by a Mr. Porteous and his wife. Mr. Porteous, a most fearsome man, literally spread terror among the pupils, marching through the classrooms with a cane, which he used vigorously and indiscriminately.[5] I was a day boy and also too young to go under Mr. Porteous and therefore had a happy, carefree time learning to read and write without any particular effort. Mr. Porteous went bankrupt (and did not even pay his church seat rent) so I was removed from his school and sent to Miss Johnson's Preparatory School, kept by a fearsome middle-aged spinster who ruled her pupils, including myself, with a rod of iron. It was for me a most miserable time. I was terrorised and the years spent at that school are among the most unhappy of my life.

My father was rather an extraordinary character. By the time I knew him, he was getting on in life, perhaps about fifty to fifty five. In those days any man over fifty had become an elderly pompous figure. Those were not the days of romping papas in shorts. Mine was an impressive figure, with a large beard, still brown, through which he boomed at his children in the manner of an oracle.

Papa had many peculiarities. He used to say that the best time of the day to be out walking was between eleven and three when the sun was at its

5 Mr Porteous's school was called Ardenlee. Baird's recollections are at odds with the wording of the school's advertisement in the *Helensburgh and Gareloch Times* in 1895, to the effect that 'Each boy receives special care and individual attention, so conducive to success in all Examinations.'

height. To come in and lunch during that time seemed quite wrong, so he lunched at three p.m. This was very logical; the hours from one to three are certainly the warmest and brightest, particularly in the all too brief winter days in Scotland. The results of Papa's logical effort were, however, devastating to the household; it meant two lunches, as the children had to go to school and their lunch had to be at one p.m. This made no matter to Papa; in those Victorian days paterfamilias was master, and his wishes were unquestionably law. Later in life I tried the three o'clock luncheon myself, being a sun lover, but the appalling trouble that arose made me drop it very promptly.

The Bairds had a strain of eccentricity running through them. It evidenced itself in my father's Rabelaisian humour and peculiar habits. My aunt Eliza Baird married an Australian millionaire,[6] and developed a mania for attending auction sales, where she bought lavishly. The whole of her large house was stacked to the roof with rubbish bought at such sales, her prize bargain being twelve dozen chamber pots!! My other aunt was not fortunate in her marriage. She married a poor farmer and their mania took the form of pets. Her house was infested by innumerable dogs, cats and fowls. She had a particular hen called Lizzie, which slept on her bed.

Dignity and decorum—without these there is but little hope of rising to high places in the church; a sense of humour must be kept in proper check and the solemnity of a judge falls far below that demanded from a Scottish minister. My father was seriously, perhaps fatally handicapped in his profession by his particular brand of humour. As a child I saw very little of this, and what I saw or heard passed completely over my head. To me my father seemed a ponderous forbidding figure. His efforts to joke with me were only frightening and embarrassing, but he was famed for his humour throughout the West of Scotland, and many stories were attributed to him; two in particular I remember.

My father had a strong dislike for marriages of necessity, common enough at one time in Scotland. He was called to officiate at one of these and arrived with reluctance and disgust half an hour late. 'You are very late Mr. Baird', said the bridegroom, 'Yes, about six months late I should think', said Mr. Baird.

My father had long since ceased to contend for the truth of the stories of the Old Testament. He had a favourite theological student, one Willie Milne—a very devout youth. 'Now Willie' said Papa, 'you believe in the literal truth of Jonah and the Whale?', 'I do indeed sir' he said. 'Aye Willie' said Papa to the astounded student, 'you and the whale rival each other in swallowing capacity'.

6 Walter Coates.

Portrait of Rev. John Baird, B.D., 1890. Baird described his father as 'rather an extraordinary character'.

The higher dignitaries of the Church regarded such episodes with apprehension and disapprobation and so Papa was passed over when they made recommendations for the higher places in the Church. He remained in his little parish, while many of his contemporaries rose from one preferment to another, and no doubt toward the end of his life this embittered him. One by one those who in his youth had looked up to him with respect and even awe, rose out of his orbit, leaving him far behind. One of his youthful circle, Bonar Law, even rose to be Prime Minister.

But Papa, in spite of his unorthodoxy, had a considerable following among the devout. I remember, when a child, being stopped in the street by a pompous member of the congregation, a man whom we children knew as 'Old Coffin Face'. 'Ah!' he said, when he met me, 'you are Mr. Baird's son are you not? I am a great admirer of your father, many times I have felt the power and emotion of his beautiful prayer at the Sabbath evening service: "On this evening of the day of grace we assemble ourselves together, O Lord, to give thanks unto Thee for the many blessings which Thou has bestowed upon us throughout the week..." and so on.' He knew it by heart, so did I, but to me it was a mere monotonous rigmarole, to him a thing of beauty and consolation—or was he in fact, as my father regarded him, a posturing mouthing old humbug?

The church dominated my life and the life of those around me; it was a living force in those days and I was an implicit believer. I thought that God was actually floating somewhere overhead, a stern man with a beard, something like Papa only of enormous dimensions, infinitely powerful and fearsome.

Fear indeed hung over me like a dark cloud in my childhood, fear not only of God but of intangible evil, ghosts and spirit creatures of unimaginable horror, waiting and watching for an opportunity to get at me.

At night I was put to bed at eight o'clock and left alone, to lie in abject terror. I covered myself with the blankets leaving only a little breathing hole, while the grey lady crept up to my bedside or the two supernatural old men crouched at the foot of my bed, waiting and watching; a burglar or tiger would have been a welcome intrusion.

Later, to the fear of ghosts was added the ever growing fear of God; I went through a phase resembling the state of mind of the Children of Israel, propitiating an angry and jealous Deity. I prayed interminably and even felt that sacrifices were demanded of me. I went on praying, fearing God and making the propitiating gestures long after my reason regarded such things as altogether contemptible and ridiculous.

By the time I was twenty I knew, or thought I knew that I was just an animal, a mechanism, a cousin of the arboreal ape. The clergy who told me I was an immortal spirit imprisoned in mortal clay I regarded as hypocrites and humbugs. The journey of life was, I knew, a meaningless pilgrimage from nothing to nowhere, 'let us eat, drink and be merry for tomorrow we die', and now after some thirty years can I add anything to these youthful beliefs? Only this—that now I am less sure of what seemed pitifully clear then, as the end grows nearer I become less certain that it must be the end, less certain of everything. The hard certainties of youth are becoming 'such stuff as dreams are made of'.

I read a great deal of everything and anything and it is interesting to consider what out of all this I have retained. There is much of Goethe's *Faust*, something of Tolstoy, much of Voltaire, much of Shakespeare's *Macbeth* and *Hamlet*. Not that these classics were my favourites, favourites came and went, Guy Boothby, Max Pemberton, W.W. Jacobs, Jerome K. Jerome, and many others, but not one line of any of these has left a trace, whereas even today, after over thirty years, I remember whole pages from the classical authors; their words bit deep.

One popular author, however, soars far above all others and takes his place among the classics. In my boyhood and youth he was a demi-god, the reading of any new book by him I regarded as a feast: this was H.G.Wells and today he still occupies a high place although he is no longer a demi-god. I have met him in the flesh and not many can submit to this ordeal and remain gods, certainly not H.G. Wells, that pleasant stubby little man with the squeaky voice. Nonetheless of the popular authors of my youth he is the only one who survives and actually takes his place among the classics.

Thus when an arrogant young man, sure and certain of the absurdity of religion, I used often to try to convert to agnosticism the clergy who came to our house as pulpit supplies. These young men fresh from the University had all the theological gambits ready for me and they met my confident spear thrusts with vast verbal smokescreens, pompous evasions, references to authorities, references to the original Greek Testament; they twisted and turned far into the night until the discussion died with the exhaustion of both parties. The older clergy baffled me by repudiating reason and intelligence alike and appealing to faith.

Social problems also preoccupied me as a boy; I saw the extraordinary phenomena of apparently decent respectable people being reduced to abject poverty and living a life of misery and despair, until semi-starvation and privation sent them to the local poor institution or the cemetery. A continual and embittered struggle for a livelihood was all around me. The poor people whom I visited with my mother lived in continual privation and fear, whereas the upper classes appeared in some mysterious manner to be secure beyond the reach of want. They did not have to earn money—it seemed to come to them automatically. When I enquired, I found they received their money from dividends, from interest on money left them by their father or relations, and as this money itself remained untouched it remained to be left to their sons; the money as it were breeding faster than the family to which it belonged. I conceived the idea of forming a fund to eliminate poverty from Scotland. The scheme was to be started by myself. I intended to make sufficient money to leave my four children (I regarded four as a reasonable number) £1,000 per annum each. The fund would be invested at compound interest and would be sufficient to allow for each of the four children living to eighty years, and at their deaths it would have augmented itself by compound interest sufficiently to allow for each of their four children having £1,000 per annum; at their deaths again each of their four children would have £1,000. The foundation fund was, in fact, to be so large that at 2½% interest it would provide for all my descendants, so that I calculated in a few hundred years the whole of Scotland would be inhabited by independent gentry.[7]

It seemed straightforward enough, but even to my childish mind there appeared a limit. Suppose my family spread over the whole earth and the world was entirely peopled by independent gentry, who would do the work? Still, it could be all right if confined to Scotland and I saw no reason why Scotland should not be peopled by independent gentlefolk, so that nothing would be heard throughout the land but the whizzing of swinging golf clubs and the plop of tennis balls, and the fruity voices of the gentry declaiming 'love-fifteen' and shouting 'fore', and their happy bell-like laughter as, in battalions, they shot down the grouse and pheasants, would ring across the glens and bens of their Scottish paradise.

The Bairds were descended originally from the Kings of Ireland. One of these gentlemen, called Sodban, was expelled from Ireland for having perpetrated a deed of indescribable obscenity. He fled to the west of Scotland and here founded a tribe which was to become known under the name of Baird.[8]

The Bairds acquired their name from the word Bard, a singer, for the Bairds were apparently a musical and romantic tribe. They also appear to have been very prolific and to have migrated from the west of Scotland to the east, as the name Baird is much more common on the east coast than on the west. In fact, there are in Edinburgh more Bairds than there are Jones's, and they run the Browns fairly close. I cannot, unfortunately, quote authorities for our origin; my father's ancestry I have not traced beyond his grandfather who was a farmer in Falkirk,[9] a place half-way between Edinburgh and Glasgow. My father himself was a bright boy, and in those days there was only one thing to do with bright boys and that was to put them into the Ministry. The great ambition of every Scottish family in the middle classes was to see their son 'wagging his head in the pulpit'.

My father did well at the University, and would have done better, so he used to say, but for the fact that he had to give a great deal of his time to tutoring so that he could augment his very small resources. However, he took his M.A. and B.D. with some distinction and later became, if not a Professor,

7 This idea is a version of distributism, an alternative to capitalism and socialism, according to which wealth is somehow divided between all individuals without state control. An exponent of distributism was G.K.Chesterton, who observed 'the problem with capitalism is that there are not enough capitalists.'

8 By his own admission, Baird had never had time to study the history of the Clan Baird. This paragraph is simply an example of his Rabelaisian sense of humour.

9 The farmhouse was a single-storey stone dwelling called 'Sunnybrae', in the Camelon district near the Dorratur Road. It is still in place but it has been greatly modernised and is surrounded by other houses.

Jessie Baird in about 1890. 'Her whole life was taken up in looking after others.' (Picture by Stuart, Helensburgh)

at least an examiner in Pastoral Theology. He was a keen student of Greek and, in his later years, of German.

My maternal grandfather, George Inglis, was an artist and earned a very precarious living. He had two brothers, Anthony and John Inglis, wealthy and successful shipbuilders in Glasgow.[10] George married a beautiful but flighty French woman and had three daughters, Elizabeth, Mary Jane and Jessie, my mother. The flighty French woman ran away and left him. George died of pneumonia; Elizabeth fell over the breakwater at Southampton and was drowned, and the two remaining orphans were adopted by his wealthy relatives, Mary Jane by a Mrs. Breen the wife of the Italian Consul in Glasgow, and Jessie (my mother) by John Inglis.

Of my mother I find it difficult to write. She was the one experience I have had of pure, unselfish devotion. Her whole life was taken up in looking after others, particularly after myself, with very little reward, unless one can accept the whole-hearted love of one small boy.

10 Until its closure in 1962 the firm of A.& J. Inglis operated a large shipyard at Pointhouse, on the Clyde. In 1947 the Inglis company built the paddle steamer *Waverley* and in 1953 it built the *Maid of the Loch* which is now berthed at the Loch Lomond Shores visitor centre, not far from Helensburgh.

First thing in the morning at 8 o'clock the children's breakfast had to be prepared. Then at 9 o'clock Papa's breakfast, then came shopping and a round of visits to the poor of the parish. When I was very young I used to accompany her on these visits and remember very clearly some of the strange and pathetic characters we called on. There was old Mrs. McCaul. All that was to be seen of her was a head wrapped in a not-too-clean nightcap and dimly seen in the darkness of a cupboard bed. Her home consisted of one very musty room which served as a kitchen, sitting room and bedroom combined. She was entirely supported by charity and lived in continual dread of being sent to the poor house. My mother visited her every day with parcels of food. While they talked I sat on a dilapidated horsehair sofa and examined a lithograph showing Jesus walking on the sea.

We also visited old Mrs. Heggie, another old and bed-ridden woman in another dingy cupboard bed. Then there were a number of poverty stricken younger women, and squalid families with tales of drunken husbands.

When the round was completed, lunch had to be prepared for the children by one o'clock. This over, another lunch had to be prepared for Papa at 3 o'clock, then high tea for the children at 5 o'clock, and all with the aid of one overworked domestic. The children had supper at 8.30, followed by Papa's at 10 o'clock. There was little leisure time but I never heard her complain. Far from it. All this work was done with a smile and cheerful willingness.

The visits to the poor had a strong effect upon me and one of my first ambitions was to make £2,000 and invest it in Government securities at 2½% so that I would have £1 a week sure and certain and be permanently beyond the reach of the workhouse.

In Helensburgh poverty was, for the most part, not the open horror of the Glasgow slums, but a horror hidden beneath the cloak of genteel respectability. The condition of the poor in city slums in my youth was appalling. I have seen young children running about in the backyards of Glasgow tenements, clothed only in old sacking in the icy wind and rain of a Glasgow winter. My blood boiled when, fresh from such sights, I used to read the society notes and see photographs of the idle rich in the pages of the 'Sketch' and 'Tatler' (usually read in dentists' waiting rooms), skiing at St. Moritz, sunbathing at Monte Carlo and flaunting their overdressed persons at race meetings and house parties.

The country could not afford to spend enough on its children to give them even the comforts and protection of the lower animals, or so the wealthy rate-payers insisted. In the Great War, however, when the security of these same wealthy rate-payers was menaced, they contrived to spend as much in a week on destruction as would have banished every slum from Glasgow.

Baird at age 12 in the garden at 'The Lodge'.

My days at Miss Johnson's came to an end when a new school was opened in Helensburgh; 'Larchfield' it was called.[11] It was a really dreadful school run by three public school men fresh from Oxford and Cambridge. They made it an imitation of their public schools and a very poor imitation it was, with all the worst features and none of the best. Sport came first and, from two till four every afternoon, we played rugby in winter and cricket in summer. After the game we stripped and went into a cold spray. This was, to us, the culminating point of a tortured afternoon. In winter it became an unbearable ordeal. I went to every subterfuge to escape but only to be found out in the end. Sooner or later a dread voice would be heard shouting 'Baird, you have not had your tub', and I would be caught by the hair of my head and held under the icy douche until I became numb and blue with cold. Then I caught chill after chill and spent most of the winter months in bed.

Among the classics Latin was my pet bugbear and I stayed year after year in the same class and term after term I translated the same Latin lesson—Fabulae-Faciles (Easy Fables) until I came to know the first story entirely by heart. Robertson, the Latin master, stormed and shouted in an effort to goad

11 Larchfield School had been founded in 1849 as Larchfield Academy. When I attended in 1947–49 it was a good and happy school. In 1977 it merged with St Bride's School (for girls) to form the co-educational Lomond School.

Baird took this picture of 'The Lodge' in 1900 with his Lizar's ¼ plate Perfecta camera. The stepping stone in front of the gate was for people alighting from horse-drawn carriages.

me into some progress, but in vain. This had rather an amusing sequel. Many years later[12] I was making a speech at the Hastings Pavilion on the occasion of its first opening to the public. When I had finished who should step on to the platform but my old master. 'Well', he said, 'I don't suppose you remember who I am?' Now was my chance to get some retaliation on my childhood torturer. I started at once with the first page of *Fabulae-Faciles*; '"Hercules alcmanae filius olim in graciae habitabat. At Juno reginae deaorum alcmanae aderat et Hercules necare voluit illigita immedi nocti", and so on' said I.[13] For thirty years that accursed rubbish had been clogging my brain; to throw it back at its instigator and watch his astounded face gave me infinite pleasure.

No form of science was taken at Larchfield and only a travesty of mathematics. The only thing I knew really well when I left that school was the first story of *Fabulae-Faciles*.

When I was at Larchfield a craze for photography seized the school. I was badly bitten by it. I saved and begged every penny I could and finally became

12 In October 1927 Baird gave a lecture on television at the White Rock Pavilion in Hastings; the building had been officially opened by the Prince of Wales in April 1927.

13 This is only a phonetic version of the quote from *Fabulae faciles;* Baird evidently did not check the spelling on the typed transcript of his dictation.

a possessor of a dream camera—'Lizar's ¼ plate Perfecta, Triple Expansion, Rack and Pinion Focusing, Rising and Falling Front, Folding Back, Taylor & Hobson F.7 rapid rectilinear lens, Bausch & Lomb roller blind shutter, 1/100th to 1/10th second'. I had the specification by heart and haven't forgotten it.

Armed with this masterpiece I was elected President of the Photographic Society. The meetings commenced with great decorum; articles were read on photography and photos taken by the members were passed round and criticised. This society was not connected with the school but included the local enthusiasts among my schoolboy friends. They are now scattered far and wide: one is world famous and a name to conjure with; Jimmy Bonner, who was killed in the first Great War; Jack Bruce, now a prosperous ship owner; Bony Wadsworth, a leading London accountant; Neil Whimster, a Glasgow shipowner; and lastly, Guy Robertson, known as 'Mephy', my life-long friend who forty years later killed himself, driven out of his mind by the World War. But 40 years ago we knew nothing of what Fate had in store for us and sat around the table at the Lodge, our world bounded by the School and the Parish, with no thoughts farther ahead than planning for the summer holidays.

At one of our meetings our discussions on photography were interrupted by X.[14] He had, it appeared, suffered a terrible insult. While innocently passing the time by instructing young Sonny Forbes how to climb a lamppost, and stimulating Sonny with application of a rubber strap, old Forbes had appeared and, unthinkable insult, boxed his ears. The club there and then were enlisted to wipe out the insult and avenge ourselves on old Forbes. Our first effort was to borrow a builder's ladder and climb to old Forbes' pigeon loft and wring the necks of all his pigeons. In cold terror I clutched the bottom of the ladder as the bold X at the top did his dastardly work on the wretched pigeons. We took the bodies down to Brown, the fishmonger, and sold them for 4d. each. Escaping undetected, we planned further vengeance. All poor old Forbes' prize tulips were ruthlessly cut down and laid in a row on his front door, the door bell was then pulled by a string, and when old Forbes came to investigate he was greeted by a volley of mud balls. The pace was, however, too hot for most of the members and resignations were tendered from all sides. In spite of a hastily passed rule that all members who resigned should be fined five shillings and receive six strokes with the cane, the club broke up.

14 The original typed version of Baird's memoirs, published in 1988, states clearly that 'X' is Jack Buchanan. He later became a star of stage and screen, and lived until 1957. When Baird was revising his memoirs, he must have felt that the disclosure of his old friend's part in this nasty prank would damage his glamorous showbusiness image.

Jack Buchanan, known to his friends as 'Chump', photographed by Baird in about 1902.

The members of the photographic society have now become, for the most part, staid and respectable members of the community. James Bonner and Guy Robertson are dead. Of the others, Jack Bruce, Bony Wadsworth and Neil Whimster are now much respected and prosperous city men. X has risen to world fame. But I may not give his name. It is strange how the pigeon episode still stands in my memory. The clear moonlight night, the rickety ladder sloping up into the darkness, the shadowy outline of a pair of legs, the wild squawkings and flutterings of the pigeons, and a voice hoarse with wrath and agitation, 'Keep that bloody ladder steady dammit!'

While I was at Larchfield I had my first and only flight. The experiments of the Wright brothers influenced the minds of Godfrey Harris and myself, and we read with eagerness all the literature available. Eventually we decided to build an aeroplane, which was a weird contraption like two box kites joined in the centre. After weeks of work it was finally completed and ready to fly, or rather glide, for it had no engine; we had decided to follow the Wright brothers' example and glide first and then, when we had mastered gliding, to fit an engine.

We hoisted our flying machine on to the flat roof of 'The Lodge' and I got into it. I had no intention of flying, but through some misunderstanding, in an excess of zeal and before I had time to give more than one shriek of alarm,

Godfrey gave the machine one terrific push and I was launched shrieking into the air. I had a few very nauseating seconds while the machine rocked wildly and then broke in half and deposited me with a terrific bump on the lawn. Fortunately, no bones were broken, but that was the first and the last time I have ever been in an aeroplane, I have no desire whatever to fly and, unless forced by circumstances, shall probably never do so.[15]

For many years Godfrey Harris was my closest friend. We went together through the intellectual upheaval which most young men experience between the ages of 16 and 20, the growing doubts as to religious beliefs, interminable arguments on metaphysics and philosophy. Well I remember the long interesting talks we had together in our student days. I think then my brain was clearer and better than it has ever been since, and the conclusions I then arrived at are the same today, only perhaps less clear now, less well understood.

We discussed the everlasting problem of free will, how every cause must have effect and, therefore, the future must be as fixed today as the past, and the events of tomorrow as fixed today as are the events of yesterday. Free will is a myth and an illusion, such was the thesis. Poor Godfrey! He was a mass of brain and initiative, but, like Mephy and myself, he had a kink. He could not stand routine work, he could not be an employee, he wanted freedom. All forms of employment irked him as forms of slavery. He went to the University and took his B.Sc. and then started business for himself in Glasgow. These efforts merely resulted in the loss of what little capital he had available. He went off to the U.S.A. where he got a job as a draughtsman and kept this job until he had saved a little money; then threw it up, bought a few acres of land for a paltry sum at a place called Wadsville in the wilds of Louisiana near the hillbillies, built himself a shack, bought a few goats and hens, planted vegetables and found himself practically self-supporting. A strange life for a B.Sc. with his only neighbours illiterate hillbillies with the mentality of goats. Their religion was, he told me, Holyrolling. After the church service, consisting of hymns and prayers, all the lights in the hall were put out and the congregation, both male and female, became possessed by the Holy Ghost, and rolled together on the floor in a vast religious ecstasy, screaming and moaning and clutching each other in the throes of their possession. The number of illegitimate births, he said, was unparalleled, but life was easy and everybody seemed satisfied and happy.

He lived himself in happy contentment for many years, pandering to goats and hens and meditating on the problems of free will and immortality, upon which he wrote me lengthy screeds at irregular intervals. Then, one morning he went out to blow up a tree root with a charge of dynamite, to get more

15 Baird never flew again. It is also of note that after 1920 he never owned or drove a car.

space for his hens and goats. The dynamite exploded prematurely and poor Godfrey was blown up with the tree stump.

At the age of 13 to 14 I was not sure what I would be. My father wanted me to be a Minister but, when he came to put forward the suggestion, with the impertinent insensibility of extreme youth, I had the audacity to tell the old gentleman that I did not think I could be a sufficiently good hypocrite. 'I think you might manage that all right', was his only reply. The thing which settled the matter of my future career was a book entitled 'The Boys Book of Stories and Pastimes'.[16] This gave an account of how to make a simple telephone with thread and cocoa tins, and then a more ambitious model with wire, nails and pill-boxes. My imagination was fired. The thread and cocoa tins instrument was soon made and proved a very poor apparatus. It was impossible to tell whether the sound was coming through the air in the ordinary way, or through the thread and tin cans. I set out to make the electrical telephone,—'Get a pill-box from a neighbouring dealer', said the book. Every dealer far and near was visited, but none had ever seen or stocked a pill-box like the one specified in the book. Nevertheless, the telephone was finally made and proved a great success. Telephones became my mania. I installed a small exchange in my room and wires were run over the street to the houses of four school friends, Neil Whimster, Jack Bruce, Ian Norwell and Godfrey Harris. More extensive plans were made, when a small tragedy brought the whole telephone enterprise to an end.

One windy night, old Macintyre the cabby was driving home when he was caught round the neck by a telephone wire, dragged from his box, and thrown cursing and shouting into the gutter. Shaking with anger, he ran to the house of Mr. McDonald, a very mild and inoffensive man, who was at that time the local manager of the National Telephone Company. 'What the devil', Macintyre demanded, 'did McDonald mean by having his blank wires hanging over the road?' 'Macintyre was going to wring his blank neck and have the law on his company'. The whole thing looked like developing into an unpleasant legal action and I had an anxious time, for the wires were not the National Telephone wires but ones running from my local exchange. Fortunately, Macintyre was a good friend of my father and the affair was settled quietly, but it was the end of the telephone exchange. This was not a very serious blow as, at this time, I was busy with an electric light installation.

The Lodge, as the local newspaper the *Helensburgh Times* put it, was 'enjoying

16 No book with this title can be traced. However *The Boys' Playbook of Science* by John Henry Pepper, revised by T.C. Hepworth (Routledge, 1885) has a detailed section on telephones including a 'nail microphone' consisting of a rusty nail resting loosely on two contacts on a sounding box. That may explain Baird's reference to nails in the next sentence.

the amenities of electric light, thanks to the ingenuity of a youthful member of the household'. I had bought a second-hand oil engine and had made a small dynamo. This charged up a battery of accumulators which, in turn, lit up the house. These accumulators consisted of innumerable lead plates wrapped in flannelette and packed in jam jars filled with sulphuric acid. I got some sort of lead poisoning when making them and have still a scar on one finger as a memento. It was about this time, that is to say in the year 1903, that the idea of trying to produce television originally occurred to me. The first thing to be done was to produce a selenium cell, and I started to make this on the kitchen range by wrapping wire round a piece of porcelain, heating this up and then rubbing with a stick of selenium. I had many trials resulting chiefly in bad smells and burnt fingers. But I did learn one thing, which was that the current from a selenium cell was infinitesimally small. Before anything could be done some means of amplifying this must be found. I made all sorts of attempts at amplifiers but could get nothing sufficiently sensitive.

This problem was solved later by the united efforts of Fleming and De Forest. It was their work which supplied the missing link and made television possible. I was, indeed, the first to produce a televised image, but without the amplifier based on Fleming's valve with De Forest's grid, I would have been hopelessly stuck.

In my early efforts to make selenium cells I got hold of Ernst Ruhmer's book 'Das Selen und seinen Bedeuten in Electral Technique',[17] which gave a very full account of Ruhmer's experiments. He really laid the foundation of the talking picture with his work of recording sound on cinema film. He also tried numerous television experiments by connecting selenium cells to shutters, with twelve selenium cells fixed to a wall, each selenium cell being connected to a shutter. By this means he could make twelve spots appear or disappear in accordance with the illumination of the selenium cells, so that he could transmit letters and numbers made by arrangement of twelve spots. Similar experiments were made in 1906 by Rignoux and Fournier. Only one book that I know of gives an account of these experiments, that is Korn und Glatzel's 'Phototelegraphie und Fernsehen' and as this is in German and out of print, it is difficult for those who have not made a close study of the subject to refute superior gentlemen who state that Baird was not the first but that television was shown by Rignoux and Fournier and others in 1906. These workers, at most, transmitted a few arrangements of spots but were far from transmitting an image by television.

By the time I was eighteen I had firmly decided to be an electrical engineer

17 The correct title of the book is *Das Selen und seine Bedeutung für die Elektrotechnik*. It was published in 1902.*

Studio portrait taken in 1912 when Baird was a student at the Royal Technical College. (W.D. Brown & Co., Helensburgh)

and, on leaving Larchfield, went to the Royal Technical College in Glasgow, filled with zeal and enthusiasm, and feeling quite sure that I would distinguish myself. I found it not so easy. There were plenty of other youths there filled with zeal and determination. How those youths worked! They were, for the most part, working men, bright lads out to make careers for themselves. They were not the intellectual cream (those won scholarships and went to the University), nevertheless, they were doughty competitors. Nothing could approach the frenzied concentration with which they absorbed learning. There was no pretence at social life—there was no time for it.[18] The first year I was there I learned a good deal that was very useful and interesting; the remaining years were, I think, almost entirely a waste of time. I learned, with great pain and boredom, masses of formulae and tedious dates, of which much was never used and soon forgotten. But what I learned in that first year has remained with me all my life and has been of very great value. My studies, however, were interrupted by frequent ill-health. This, combined with simple lack of ability and stupidity, held me back, so that it took me five years to get the Associateship of the College—a course which an able and energetic youth could take in three years.

In my studies I did one sensible thing. I went to Glasgow University and took the final course for the B.Sc. and had the sense not to make any effort whatsoever to do any work, but gave myself up entirely to the social life of the students. I had a very enjoyable time and many pleasant memories, instead of what I should otherwise inevitably have had, a nervous breakdown. I had, in the back of my mind, the intention of sitting for the B.Sc. examination at a later date, but life proved much too crowded for any folly of that sort. Furthermore, the war broke out and gave me an excellent alibi. I was engaged on war work—no time for study.

18 Baird may have exaggerated the lack of social life at the Royal Technical College. It had a thriving student magazine to which he frequently contributed humorous articles. In 1964 the college became the University of Strathclyde and in 1992 the university awarded an honorary degree to Margaret Baird.

Chapter Two

When I left school I went immediately to the Royal Technical College, Glasgow, travelling up and down from Helensburgh. The Technical College was an extremely efficient national institute. The students were, for the most part, poor young men desperately anxious to get on. They worked with an almost unbelievable tenacity and zeal. There were, however, a few exceptions, gentlemen's sons, well off and with no real anxieties as to their future. Among these was a tall well-built youth, the son of the Moderator of the Presbyterian Church,[1] by name John Reith.[2]

I met him for the first time in rather unfavourable circumstances. I was, and still am, very short-sighted and, at the beginning of one of the classes, the Professor asked if those who were short-sighted and wanted front seats would hand in their names. When I went up to the platform to give him my name, three large impressive young students were talking to him. They talked on terms of equality; in fact there was a distinct aroma of patronage. The young gentlemen were of the type we would today call 'heavies', and they boomed with heavy joviality at the poor little Professor who was distinctly embarrassed and ill at ease. I interrupted timidly and handed him a piece of paper with my name on it. As I did so, the heaviest and most overpowering of the three 'heavies' turned round and boomed at me 'Ha! what is the matter with you? Are you deaf or blind?' I simpered something in inaudible embarrassment and he turned his back on me, and the three 'heavies' walked out of the classroom booming pretentiously to each other.

This was the first time I saw Reith. I did not see him again for twenty years. Reith did not distinguish himself in his examinations; he was worse than I was, without the excuse of ill-health, but now we see him a Cabinet Minister and a national figure, while those who soared above him at college are lost in obscurity, little provincial professorlings,[3] draughtsmen, petty

1 Rev. George Reith was a minister of the Free Church of Scotland, not to be confused with the Church of Scotland.

2 John Charles Walsham Reith (1889–1971) served as first Director General of the B.B.C. between 1922 and 1938. He was a Cabinet Minister between 1940 and 1942, but he and Winston Churchill disliked each other.

3 This contemptuous phrase was coined by H.G.Wells in his short story 'Filmer'(1901).

departmental chiefs and the like. The examiners awarded no marks for impressive appearances, no marks for oracular booming voices, no marks for influential relatives. To the examiners an overpowering 'heavy' and a lean rat-faced little creature were all alike. All they were concerned with was the capacity to absorb knowledge and regurgitate it onto an examination paper. Had marks been given for personality and for moving in exclusive circles (superlatively valuable in the business of getting on), Reith would undoubtedly have topped the examination list. The great acquisition of knowledge counts for little in the battle of life. Francis Bacon summed up the matter in his essay on Metaphysics:—'Wouldst thou acquire riches? The rule is simple —make many friends'. That is the first rule, it being understood that the friends move in the right circles, influential friends, but any friends are better than none. God help the recluse who lusts for worldly success!

I did not do well at the Royal College but managed finally to become an Associate and to get the College diploma. It took me five years to do this. I do not think it was altogether stupidity, for my studies were continually interrupted by long illnesses. Interspersed between my studies were periods when I served as an apprentice engineer. My first experience was in Halley's Industrial Motors at Yoker. I went there full of zeal and determination to get on, but my ardour was very soon damped. The works opened at 6 o'clock in the morning and closed down nominally at 5.30, but in practice there was incessant overtime and it was seldom that I was free much before 8.00. The work was absolutely soul-destroying, monotonous drudgery. The first job I got was to chip, with a chisel, little grooves in each of a great pile of castings. I remember they were called 'Spring Housings'. Week after week I chipped these little grooves, with all around me the most sordid conditions and, in the winter, icy cold. The result was that my work was punctuated by perpetual ill-health. This was, I think, in 1909 and the Great War had not yet appeared on the horizon.[4]

While I was at the Lodge I had been under the most strict supervision and, although the years I spent with telephones and decrepit tri-cars were among the happiest of my life, one thing marred this happiness—in common with many young men I suffered considerably from suppressed desire. In Helensburgh, in my circumstances, it was difficult to speak with a young lady and as to a love affair, well that was entirely out of the question. This did not greatly worry me. Self-denial, for a time, I could put up with. All would be well when I went into digs and got away from supervision and threw off the yoke.

4 Baird's apprenticeship at Halley's Industrial Motors lasted from May 1910 to February 1911. A testimonial letter from the Shop Foreman (W. MacFarlane) recommended him as 'a very industrious, sober and efficient workman.'

I thought that when I left home I would throw off all restraint and become a soul untrammelled. 'Then would I quench my glowing passions in a sensual sea, nor in the shallows dabble'.[5] I was to find, however, that I was not of the stuff of which Don Juans are built; I tried hard, but circumstances and temperament were hopelessly against me. I had been told by other students that it was easy; you simply walked out in the evening and, when you saw a young lady who appealed to you, you merely walked beside her for a few paces, remarked 'Good evening,' and the rest followed. I tried it and, in a state of complete nervousness, bungled it hopelessly and got the snub I deserved, returning home in a state of nervous collapse. My dreams of Don Juan and the sensual seas showed no hope of realisation. Strumpets were thoroughly repulsive. The idea disgusted me. Finally, in desperation, I took out the landlady's neice, a gaunt raw-boned creature. I was determined to have an affair at all costs. In a quiet spot I endeavoured to embrace this gawky trollop. A drop of mucous hung from her long red nose. She laughed harshly, showing a row of decayed teeth and grunted 'Hands off the beef', digging her bony elbow into me.

Even this grotesque travesty of womanhood would have nothing to do with me! My technique was as hopeless as my opportunities were confined. Later I became more adroit, but it forms a sorry tale.[6] Futile and frustrated, opportunity passed me by. The years of youth and romance were lost in sordid and mean lodgings, in soul-destroying surroundings under grey skies. What waves of jealous anger and hate passed over me as I saw in the *Tatler* photographs of happy bands of the youth of the rich in house parties, skiing parties, sun bathing parties, dancing parties, while I trudged to work in the cold dawn with sordid, miserable and grim poverty on every side, coughing and choking, either sickening for a cold or trying to recover from one. What a wave of resentment and anger comes over me even now, when I think of the awful conditions of work in those Glasgow factories—the sodden gloom, the bitter bleak, cold rain, the slave-driven workers cooped in a vile atmosphere with the incessant roar and clatter of machinery from six in the morning to six at night, and then home to lodgings surrounded by sordid squalor, too worn out to move from my miserable bedroom.

I was encouraged by the knowledge that for me it was only a passing phase. I was, or believed I was, a short-term prisoner, but if I had been like most of the poor creatures who worked with me, in for a life sentence, I should certainly have become an anarchist and taken part with zeal in anything which would have mended—or ended—my lot. I should have joined any

5 Lines from a translation of Goethe's *Faust*.*

6 This is a cryptic reference to his affair with 'Alice' between 1921 and 1931.*

modern Guy Fawkes and blown to hell His Most Gracious Majesty the King, the Royal Family and all the Lords and Commons, in the firm belief that, whatever happened, nothing, not even death, could be worse than the fate to which these, my callous and indifferent rulers, had doomed me. Such was my embittered outlook. The men themselves were not socialists. They were, for the most part, indifferent and took their conditions as an inevitable natural phenomenon, like the long and bitter winter weather, miserable but unalterable.

The journeyman who worked next to me and who was immediately responsible for me, was a fierce old man known as Big Gibson and described as a 'callous old bastard'. He was an independent and vindictive socialist with the most lurid flow of foul language, unfortunately mostly unprintable even in these days of obscene novels. I was accustomed to outbursts such as 'Whit the hell are ye standin' gapin' there for? Dae ye take this for a bloody Sunday school treat?' (I have modified the adjectives).

The chief of the research room was a public school and university man and endeavoured to keep some of his refinement. On one occasion he had the temerity to offer a piece of advice to Big Gibson. Big Gibson considered this an insufferable impertinence and I remember to this day the flood of abuse which descended on the superior research gentleman as he fled, followed by a roar of 'Get to hell, ye hauf biled toff'. He complained to the manager, who got on well with Big Gibson and rebuked him gently—'Aye George, that's fine! You knock the bloody guts oot o' the stuck-up bastard. Then you get the sack and your wife and wains starve. Keep your daunder doon, the poor beggar does his best!' There it was—lose your job and you and your family starve. There was no dole in those days.

I completed my course at the Royal Technical College and took my Associateship in 1914 and did one of the most sensible things of my early manhood. The Associateship of the Technical College qualified one to take the B.Sc. at Glasgow University after six months attendance. With some difficulty I persuaded my long-suffering parents to let me take this course. Those six months were one of the happiest times in my life. I had the sense not to endeavour to cram and did the absolute minimum of work, while heartily enjoying the society of my fellow students. We had innumerable outings in the happy atmosphere that can only be found among students.

Glasgow University is, I believe, a very plebeian institution compared to Oxford or Cambridge, but after the Technical College it seemed a perfect paradise. In the middle of my course[7] the War broke out. It was expected at

7 World War I started in August, 1914. Baird entered Glasgow University in the autumn of 1914, sharing the popular belief that the war would not last long; he left the university in March 1915.

first, and confidently predicted, that it would be over in a few months, Germany would give way, Germany would crack, Germany could not stand the strain; but it dragged on. Urged by some sense of duty, or possibly by the desire to appear well in the eyes of my friends, I presented myself at the recruiting office. A red-faced Glasgow 'keelie' in a badly fitting uniform stood at the door. 'Upstairs. First to the left', he shouted in a very broad accent. Upstairs a raw and very nervous young man sat by the door, while at a desk a young officer filled up forms one by one. 'Take that pipe out of your mouth!' he roared at one lout who was endeavouring to show his sangfroid by puffing vigorously; 'Name, age, occupation? Now then! In there for medical examination'.

The medical examiner, a shrewd looking old gentleman, examined my skinny form with sad and disapproving eyes, tapped my scanty chest and placed his ear to listen to my wheezy breathing. An assistant ran a tape measure round me and shouted the paltry inches with contempt. 'Do you suffer from colds very much?' said the doctor. 'Yes', said I, 'a great deal'. 'Every winter you are knocked up, I suppose?' he asked, then grunted, 'Aye aye umphm! You can dress now'. He went to his desk and wrote something on a piece of paper, then stamped it with a large rubber stamp. When I examined it, I read in large red letters 'Unfit for any service'. I buttoned up my waistcoat and went downstairs. The red-faced 'keelie' was surprised. 'Hallo', he said 'what's up? You're back quick'. 'Yes', I said, 'I am unfit for any service'. 'You're lucky', he ejaculated, 'What about the price of a pint?' I gave him a shilling and took my way to the tram—lucky to be unfit for any service![8]

When I left the University I answered an advertisement and obtained a job as Assistant Mains Engineer in the Clyde Valley Company. I was stationed in the Rutherglen area, and my job was to go out and supervise the repairing of any breakdowns. I had a telephone in my bedroom and, if the electrical supply failed, I had to get out of bed and attend to it. It was a horrible job. My memory conjures up visions of standing the whole night in the rain, cold and miserable, while Stibbs, the chief ganger, and his men, dug holes in the road to find faulty cables. Trying to placate a gang of truculent Irish labourers at 4 o'clock in the morning, when they wanted to stop the job and go home, was anything but pleasant. Sometimes in the nights drunken fights started. I remember one particular night Jimmy McGauchy knocking Billie MacIlvaney down a manhole and both finally departing with roars of pain and anger and volleys of cursing, and all the time steady rain falling and a bitter wind

8 Baird's army medical card, stamped 'Unfit for Any Service' is dated April 17, 1916. Therefore he had already been with the Clyde Valley Electric Power Company for about a year when he went to the recruiting office.*

At the Clyde Valley Co. power station in 1915. Baird has stuffed handkerchiefs up both his sleeves, ready to deal with his frequent colds. 'It was a horrible job'.

blowing. Sordid miserable work, punctuated by repeated colds and influenza. I wanted more money. I got 30/- a week and I was unable to get a better job because I was always ill. Finally I decided it was hopeless and I had better try and start some business which was less strenuous and in which I would be my own master.

It was a wise decision. If I had remained travelling along the straight road of an engineering career I would either have been dead by now or a hopeless, broken-spirited object. To break my career seemed to those about me the act of an irresponsible madman, throwing away all my expensive training. But if the choice was between hopeless slavery and madness, I preferred madness—there seemed no middle course. 'Are there no ways but these alone, madman or slave must man be one?'[9] It seemed so in my case. If I remained an

9 The lines are from Matthew Arnold's poem 'A Summer Night'. The correct quotation is 'Is there no life, but these alone? Madman or slave, must man be one?'

engineer I saw nothing before me but a vista of grey days, of unrelieved drudgery, coughing and shivering through the winters with no hope of forcing my way through the mob of lusty competitors. Nairn, the chief engineer, had summed up my chances. 'We cannot give Baird a better job—he is always ill', and so I saw myself as the years went by, working through one wet winter after another until at last one of my winter chills would bring the sorry story to an end.

I determined, at all costs, to 'depart on the wide ocean of life anew',[10] but it was not easy. Most of the recognized avenues were closed to me through want of health and money. I decided however to start in business for myself. My first thought was to market a cure for piles for which Billy Barnes, one of the station attendants, claimed to have a specific, a mysterious white compound which he claimed to be an infallible cure.

Billy had been a stud groom, but had given it up after an accident which had resulted in his being lame in one leg. In the stud in which Billy was employed he was in charge of a stallion called 'The Duke of Marlborough'. The Duke was past his prime and not in demand, but it occurred to Billy to use him to get the mares ready for service by the other stallions. So, one day Billy put his idea into practice, leading the mares as they arrived to the box of the Duke, who was allowed to nose them and get them (and incidentally himself) into a proper condition of excitement. The mares were then led away to the other stallions and the Duke was left to cool himself as best he could. Towards the end of the day the Duke lost his temper and kicked his box to pieces, knocking Billy down and trampling on him, breaking his leg as well as other damage.

Unfortunately for Billy's Pile Cure project, I was a chronic sufferer and tried it on myself with such devastating results that I was unable to sit down for nearly a week.

About this time I had carried out an experiment which hastened my career with the Clyde Valley to its close. I had an idea for making diamonds.[11] Diamonds are created in nature by subjecting carbon to a very high pressure and a very high temperature. I thought I might get these conditions artificially by electrically exploding a rod of carbon embedded in concrete. I got a thick carbon bar and filed it down into a thin rod in the centre, then I attached a wire to each end and embedded the whole thing in a large iron pot. I connected the wires to a switch which, when closed, put them straight across the power station bus bars. My idea was to pass a stupendous sudden current through the carbon so as to generate enormous heat and pressure. I chose a

10 Another quotation from Matthew Arnold's 'A Summer Night'.

11 This idea may have come from H.G.Wells's short story 'The Diamond Maker' (1905).

good time and then, when no-one was about, closed the switch. There was a dull thud from the pot, a cloud of smoke, and then the main current breaker tripped and the whole of the power supply went off. I had anticipated this and soon got it going again, but I did not get my wires away quickly enough and unpleasant explanations followed. Thereafter I was regarded as a dangerous character and, in the general unpleasantness, I forgot about the pot and it disappeared. Perhaps it is today lying in some forgotten rubbish heap, a pot of cement with priceless diamonds embedded in it.

Having decided to be a madman I retained the maximum amount of method in my madness and, before finally throwing up my job, commenced to lay the foundations of my independent enterprise. The scheme I finally decided upon was 'The Baird Under-sock', 'Medicated, soft, absorbent, worn under the ordinary sock, keeps the feet warm in winter and cool in summer'.

I suffered from cold feet and was certain I had found a cure, which was to take off my socks and wrap a sheet of newspaper round my bare feet, and then put the sock on again over the paper. Cold feet are invariably caused by damp. The need for watertight boots is realized, but the need for dry socks is often overlooked. Socks in the ordinary way are always slightly damp. Take a pair of socks out of a drawer and hold them in front of the fire and feel the extraordinary amount of moisture they contain. To cure cold feet, make your socks absolutely dry by heating to the point of burning; even then in a few hours your feet may feel cold again. Take off your socks and you will, in all probability, find them damp again. Then if you again heat them and dry them and put a piece of thick paper between the socks and foot your feet will again become warm. It took me some years to discover this simple fact, but what a comfort warm feet are, only cold feet sufferers can realise. I always suffered from cold feet, even as a boy, and I used to think how pleasant it would be if the surface of the globe were covered with three inches of warm water, so that my feet would always be warm.

Having found the cure the problem was to market it. Paper undersocks were not feasible, so I approached a sock maker and, after many wanderings, discovered two things. Firstly, the trade does not recognise such things as socks. Socks are known as 'Gents half-hose'. Secondly, the home of 'Gents half-hose' is Hinkley in Yorkshire. From Hinkley I got six dozen specially made, unbleached half-hose. Then I sprinkled these with borax and put them in large envelopes printed with 'The Baird Undersock' and containing a pamphlet describing their advantages and containing testimonials. I then took a one-roomed office at 196 Vincent Street and inserted an advertisement in the *People's Friend* for 'The Baird Undersock, Medicated, Soft, Absorbent. Keeps the feet warm in winter and cool in summer. 9d. per pair, post free'.

I got one reply enclosing 9d. As the advertisement had cost me 30/- this was not promising, and so one Saturday afternoon I packed two dozen pairs of socks in a handbag and set out on my first venture as a commercial traveller. I visited chemists and drapers and sold the two dozen and got orders for six dozen more, and felt that at last I was on the road to success. Not advertising, but travelling, that was the key.

I put an advertisement in the *Glasgow Herald*—'Traveller wanted, visiting chemists and drapery stores, to carry sideline'. The advertisement brought me dozens of replies and soon, throughout Scotland and as far down as London, travellers were carrying the 'Baird Undersock'. I sold very few in England. Selfridge's bought six dozen and so did a few others in London and the provinces, but in Glasgow I did well as I could interview and supervise my travellers.

I began to get a little money together and spent some on publicity. I sent a squad of women round with sandwich boards and got my first taste of what is known as editorial publicity. They were news, and photographs of them appeared in some of the illustrated papers with the caption: 'First sandwich women in Glasgow', 'New occupation for the ladies', and such like headings. The name 'Baird Undersock' appeared prominently on the placards. Some of the newspapers published this without comment, but in two cases I had to pay a small fee to have the name reproduced in the paper. It was first-class publicity.

Shortly after this news of my activities began to percolate through to the

Advertising the Baird Undersock (1). The women with sandwich boards.

Advertising the Baird Undersock (2). A plywood replica of a tank, complete with side guns, was pushed along the street by a man walking inside it.

Clyde Valley Head Office. I thought that the end was near and sent in my resignation; I was only just in time to forestall getting the sack.

I was now completely on my own resources, but the 'Baird Undersock' was well under way and bringing me considerable profits. The undersocks were doing pretty well in the chemists, but most of the money was made in the drapery stores. I sold a dozen pairs to the Polytechnic (the Selfridges of Glasgow). The buyer who had bought them out of curiosity, I think, more than anything else, did not make any effort to exhibit them and when I went round later I saw no trace of the 'Baird Undersock' anywhere in the store. So I induced a number of my friends to call round at the Polytechnic and ask for 'the Baird Undersock', supplying them with cash for purchasing. The result was the undersocks were immediately sold out and the drapery counter was besieged by people demanding 'Baird Undersocks'. The effect was electrical. The buyer himself called three times at my little office, only to find it closed, but he left a note and I called at the Polytechnic and sold him on the spot fifty dozen pairs. He had a special table at one of the entrances and one of the front windows was filled with 'Baird Undersocks'. The result was, of course, an immediate rush by the inquisitive public. Not only so, but Copland and Lye and the other big stores immediately wanted to be in on this new line which was booming at the Polytechnic. My whole stock was sold out at once and I booked further substantial orders. It occurred to me to add other sidelines to the undersock and I had a business in boot polish, solid scent and other sundries. But before long my old trouble recurred and in the early spring I was laid up with a very bad cold.

In the summer of 1919, Baird bought a powerful motorcycle with some of his earnings from the Baird Undersock. 'Mephy' Robertson is sitting on the side-car.

The business suffered terribly as it was a one-man show and, on my recovery, I determined to go abroad and escape the Scottish winter with its accompanying devastating illnesses.

Chapter Three

Godfrey Harris had been out to Trinidad and had sent me glowing accounts of the possibilities there. I got a number of guide books filled with equally laudatory descriptions. 'Ierie, land of the humming bird[1] and eternal summer', —that was how they described it—'the Caribbean Paradise'. I decided to close down the Baird Undersock Company and try my luck in the Caribbean Paradise.[2] I found when I wound up the company that I had made roughly £1,600, that is to say in twelve months of business on my own I had made more than I would have made in twelve years as a Clyde Valley engineer. I was full of optimism and set out blithely for the West Indies, taking a cheap passage in a cargo boat so as to keep as much as possible of my capital intact. I had three trunks filled with samples of cotton and other goods to sell to the natives. I began, however, to feel a little doubtful of the prospects during the voyage.

A hard bitten native of Venezuela inspected my samples and seemed to think my prospects of selling them infinitesimal. He regarded me as little short of a madman to give up a good business in Glasgow for a wild-cat venture in the tropics. I arrived at Port of Spain after three very unpleasant weeks in a heaving cargo boat.

Before we landed the captain gave me some advice. 'A young virile man in these warm climates regards regular visits to lady friends as essential as regular visits to the W.C., and so,' said the captain, 'they don't last more than a year or so. Black velvet and cocktails, that's the life that winds them up. Keep off it. The whole West Indies are rotten with venereal. This is the home of venereal. Christopher Columbus and his lads imported it to Europe from the West Indies. They introduced it to Europe just as Raleigh introduced the potato.' And so, with this dire warning ringing in my ears, I disembarked.

1 This was the picturesque name given to Trinidad by the native Carib people, before the arrival of Columbus in 1498.

2 In 1919 Baird was in love with 'Alice' and one of his aims in going to Trinidad was to build up his health and his business prospects so that he could marry her. But in June 1920, while he was still in Trinidad, she married another man.*

The moist heat rose in waves from the crowded pavement; negroes, Chinese, Caribs, Hindoos, Portuguese and a few sallow-faced Europeans jostled me on the narrow side path as we walked towards the Ice House Hotel, where Harris had booked a room for me.

I was glad to get there and get on top of the bare bed in the little carpetless bedroom. I did not feel well and soon I felt worse and, for the next few days, I was very ill indeed. I had contracted some form of dysentery. Most Europeans get it sooner or later, I was told. I had not lost much time. It left me weak and miserable and with my faith in the islands of the blessed considerably shaken.

However, as soon as I could get about I transferred to the boarding house of Mrs. Brisbane, 'Columbia House'. Here I was met by Mrs. Brisbane herself, a fat old woman with a yellow face of almost unimaginable ugliness. She was, however, full of compassioned kindliness. 'Come in, come in, we'll take care of you here. I'll be a mother to you!'

I must indeed have looked a pitiful wreck. The other inmates of this asylum for white cargo were three young bank clerks, one in bed with a venereal affliction; a young commercial traveller who had been sent out to Trinidad to cure him of dipsomania; and lastly, an incongruous figure, an elderly, very prim and proper English governess. She had lost her job and been left stranded in Port of Spain.

I shared a large bedroom with the dipsomaniac. He had only recently

Baird in rural Trinidad in early 1920, with his 20 h.p. Ford Runabout.

come out from London and, knowing nothing of his background, I thought this a lucky meeting, for he was a most amiable fellow and most anxious to help me. I felt he would be a help and opened my heart and my trunk of samples for his inspection. I was rather disappointed to note that, anxious as he was to encourage me, my scheme of selling to the natives did not seem to fill him with enthusiasm. However, he said he would himself take some of my samples round and as he was well in with the chief buyers, might be able to place some orders. He also gave me the names of some buyers upon whom I should call. I set out next day and met with a complete fiasco. I will not dwell on it. After three weeks of interviewing greasy negroes, half-caste Portuguese, tipsy whites, and generally having a thoroughly humiliating time, the net result was the sale of 5 lbs. of safety pins, my one and only sale. What was to be done now?

While I was meditating I got ill again. A high fever kept me in bed for a week. While in bed I conceived the idea of starting a jam factory. The island teamed with citrus fruits and guavas seemed plentiful. Sugar was produced on the island in great quantity. Why not mix these products into jam and so export it in a form in which it would not be liable to rot? The island also was overrun with mango trees, and so mango chutney could be added to the factory's products. Here before me was a fortune waiting to be picked up. I found that the centre of the fruit growing area was at a little native village in the Santa Cruz Valley, a place called Bourg Mulatrice (The Black Man's Village). Here I got a room cheap in a house belonging to the local cocoa planter,[3] a wooden building beside a small river surrounded by a clump of gigantic bamboos, in the very heart of the bush. With the help of Ram Roop[4] (a Hindu youth) and Tony (a large simple creature of mixed generation), I commenced to build a factory.

The first thing to do was to find a suitably large pot in which to boil the jam. A scrap merchant in Port of Spain sold me a large copper pan, originally I believe a wash tub, big enough to hold 1 cwt.[5] of jam. Underneath this we built a brick fireplace, complete with chimney, and started off with the cauldron filled with sugar and orange cuttings in the proportions specified in the cookery books. We then lit a fire and Ram Roop armed himself with one of two large spade-like wooden stirrers and I took the other. We stirred

3 The plantation was owned by a Mr. Stollmeyer. Baird paid no rent for the factory site and he stayed nearby at the house of the plantation manager, a Mr. Fitzgerald, at a cost of $40 (about £8) per month for room and board.

4 The surname Ramroop (one word) occurs quite frequently in Trinidad and it is possible that this was really the name of Baird's assistant.

5 1 cwt is the old measure 'a hundredweight', or 112 lb (51 kg).

The jam factory at Bourg Mulatrice. It is fenced in with wire netting and the brick fireplace and chimney are on the right of the picture. The copper cauldron is partly visible behind the door. (Hastings Museum and Art Gallery).

vigorously. The heat became terrific. I took off everything but my trousers. The sugar melted and the jam began to simmer. We continued to stir vigorously, as instructed by the text books. Sweet smelling clouds of vapour rose from the pot and floated into the jungle. They acted like a trumpet call to the insect life and a mass of insects of all shapes and sizes appeared out of the bush in terrifying numbers. They flew into the steam above the cauldron in their thousands and, scorched, fell lifeless into the boiling jam. I dropped my stirrer and ran, but Ram Roop did not seem the least perturbed. After the first wild charge the insect stream abated a little and, finally, we finished our boiling of jam and poured it into a selection of glass jam jars. I had, however, calculated without the insects. The factory became an insects' paradise. Hundreds of enormous ants invaded us and, in one night, made away with 1 cwt. of sugar. The floor of my bedroom swarmed with insects, chiefly enormous cockroaches; great spiders ran up and down the walls, and weird insects whose names I did not know flew in and out in swarms, whilst mosquitoes continually enfolded me in a cloud.

We sold some pots of jam, with difficulty, to the local stores, then I fell ill with fever. Ram Roop and Tony carried on while I gave instructions from my bed. But there seemed to be no adequate market for our wares in Port of Spain and I decided, when I was able to move about again, to return to London and endeavour to establish a market there. I bought a large cask and a number of kerosene tins and packed them with mango chutney, guava jelly, marmalade and tamarind syrup. Complete with this cargo I set sail for London more dead than alive and with more than three-quarters of my capital gone. The West Indies is an excellent spot for those in robust health who can stay at the Queen's Park Hotel and spend their time in bathing and motoring, but living in the bush, particularly under the trees in a valley near a river, is not at all a wise course of procedure.

While I was in Port of Spain I met a very agreeable companion, Harold Pound,[6] and for part of the time I was there we shared a bungalow and spent much of our time drinking gin cocktails and whisky. I remember one evening coming back to find Pound with a large whisky and soda before him, gaping with alcoholic horror at a stupendous, unbelievably large grasshopper which sat on the table gaping back at him. He was immensely relieved when I arrived and confirmed that the grasshopper was real and not the result of alcohol. We finally caught the creature in a waste paper basket. It proved to be a gigantic locust and we kept it in a canary's cage as a pet for the amusement of the people who visited us. We fed it on grass and whisky and soda, which it drank feverishly. However, it soon died, probably of delirium tremens.

When I returned to London Pound accompanied me. I think he was a little concerned about my future. He knew more of London than I did and saw my jam venture in something approaching its true perspective. Before the journey was over I began myself to find my first optimism more than a little diminished, but there was nothing for it but to see the thing through. I took a small shop at 166 Lupus St.[7] and there, in due course, the mango chutney and other delicacies arrived. I visited Mark Lane and Mincing Lane trying to find a market for my wares. Nobody wanted mango chutney and nobody appeared to want the guava jelly; the quality was not up to standard. Finally, in desperation, I sold the whole stock to a sausage maker to mix up with the other material which went into his sausages. He gave me £15 for the lot. The trouble now was to find some means of making money.

When I first arrived in London I went straight to a boarding house in Bloomsbury kept by a Miss Selina Borthwick.[8] It had been recommended to me by Mephy, who was staying there, and opened my eyes to what Bloomsbury boarding houses can be. The charges were from 25/- upwards for partial board, which meant breakfast and dinner throughout the week, and breakfast,

6 Actually Robert Pound.*

7 The shop was at 131 Lupus Street, not 166.* The address is now that of the Pimlico Housing Estate Office.

8 The boarding house was at 19 Endsleigh Street and was owned by Miss Caroline Borthwick.*

Baird is the best-dressed member of the group outside 131 Lupus Street, some time in 1921. The door leading to his business premises is on the extreme right of the picture.

lunch and supper on Sundays. It was an appalling place. Wishing to cut down expenses, I obtained one of the cheapest rooms at 25/-. This was a wretched attic at the top of the house with one little barred window with broken glass, a bare floor and a rickety bed, and some dilapidated blankets. I will say, however, that the blankets were clean. For breakfast we had, usually, ham and bread and butter. Occasionally, the ham was joined by an egg of doubtful quality. Dinner, as a rule, was some soup of the dishwater type, followed by a watery stew with mashed potato, followed by some sort of pudding which I usually found was better left alone. The inmates were the most depressing crew I have ever met—down and out commercial travellers and wretched elderly women, some eking out an existence on small pensions, others employed as milliners and stenographers and so on, grown old in service and hanging on in constant fear of the sack.

I would not have stayed at all but for Mephy, who seemed to find the place very convenient and cheap and got on well with Selina. Poor Mephy was also cutting down expenses and had a bed in a disused washing house, with stone floor and original wash tub. The wash tub still had the hot and cold taps, so that at least he had the advantage of a supply of hot water. It was a dreadful place to sleep in however, very damp and cold, and I think it contributed to give him the rheumatics from which he suffered.

My capital, in spite of extreme economy, had diminished to approximately £200. It was time to get some money-making project under way. I tried answering the advertisements which appeared in *The Times* as 'Business Opportunities' and all sorts of queer characters appeared at my lodgings, with schemes as queer as themselves. Not one single reasonable proposition resulted. The majority of the business opportunities were one form or another of patent medicines. One man, however, gave me some trouble. He had a scheme for buying up surplus Army stock and he wanted me to put up £1,000 to buy an enormous quantity of galvanized iron buckets which, according to him, were going at an absolutely throw-away price. These buckets were to be sold from street barrows. The barrow trade was to be organised by a friend of his who accompanied him and was, he said, known as the 'King of the barrows' throughout London and had the whole barrow trade at his finger tips. He was an enormous villainous looking hooligan in a red muffler and very much the worse for drink. When I showed some hesitancy in parting with £1,000 on the spot the two gentlemen became very obstreperous and I had some difficulty in getting them to leave the house. Not one single reasonable proposition resulted.

I heard that Australian honey could be bought at a very low price as considerable quantities of it were lying in the docks and the owners were anxious to clear at almost any price. I took a gamble and bought two tons. This I stored at Lupus Street and advertised in *The Times* and the *Morning Post*:—'28 lb. tins finest Australian honey, post free to your address 30/-'.[9] This was a very paying venture. I got streams of replies and began once more to make money instead of losing it.

I spent a good deal of my time going round Mark Lane looking for bargains. There were any amount of gentlemen offering such opportunities. These gentlemen were known as Mark Lane scorpions. They had many unpleasant tricks but their favourite was to get money in advance to clinch some wonderful bargain and then disappear. Sometimes they took jobs as travellers, sold your goods at absurd prices (promising the customers enormous discount) then, immediately the goods were delivered they called, collected the cash and vanished.

At this juncture Harold Pound again appeared on the scene and introduced

9 Advertisements for the honey were placed between 17 September 1921 and 4 February 1922.*

me to his uncle, who owned a little horticultural business which included a small shop and large storage accommodation.[10] He wanted to get rid of it and, finally I bought it from him for, I think it was, £100 cash. This business was just what I wanted. It gave me storage accommodation in plenty and a certain amount of over-the-counter trade. The old customers still continued to come and I did my best to sell them fertilisers in the midst of the honey business. The place was most unhealthy, the office being built under a railway bridge and the walls running with damp. The business, however, was paying, and I had a number of other schemes on hand, including a corner in coir fibre dust, when my old enemy laid me low again and I found myself in bed with my usual severe cold. In bed I remained for several weeks, the business meanwhile going to bits. While I was in this state a visitor arrived from Trinidad—a friend of Pound's. He was anxious to start up in London and offered to buy from me a half interest in my little business. I willingly agreed and, while I was in bed, he took charge. My cold did not get better and finally I went to Buxton on the doctor's advice. My partner then bought me out of the business, paying me £100 cash and £200 in shares in an Oil Company—(I still have them. They were, and remained, unsaleable). Fortunately, I had insured myself at the beginning of the year against illness and all the time I was in Buxton—in fact all the time I was ill—I was paid by the insurance company £6 a week. I was ill for nearly six months, but finally recovered sufficiently to go back to London.

So once more I found myself with no business and, this time, with little more than £l00 in my pocket. I settled in lodgings in Pembroke Crescent[11] and commenced looking through the papers for some opening.

In the *Grocer* I saw an advertisement offering two tons of Resin Soap at what seemed to me an amazingly low price. I followed this up and my chasing of the bargain led me to the office of H.T. Manning. He himself was out, but his lady secretary was entertaining to a cup of tea an elderly gentleman with pince-nez glasses (from which one glass was missing). She kindly invited me to join them and we discussed the soap trade. The resin soap, it appeared, was rubbish and not to be touched at any price. But, Mr. Young could put me on a good line—a fortune in it if handled the right way. And so, with Mr. Young as Manager at £2 per week, I took a one-roomed office at 13, Water Lane, placed an order with Messrs. George Green Ltd., for one ton twin tablet, double wrapped pale yellow soap, to be delivered to my instructions. I advertised for travellers and set Mr. Young 'on the road' complete with the

10 The business was William Herbert and Co., at 28 Southwark Street, located beneath the main railway line between Cannon Street and Waterloo stations.* The address is now a cab office.

11 7 Pembridge Crescent, Notting Hill Gate.*

Soon after the recovery of his health at Buxton, Baird visited Helensburgh for the wedding of his sister Jean and the Rev. Neil Conley on 6 June 1922. In this picture of the reception at the Queen's Hotel, Baird is first from the right in the back row. His parents are seated on either side of the bridal pair and his sister Annie, wearing a large hat, is behind the groom.

first sample of 'Baird's Speedy Cleaner'. I sat in my office and awaited events. I had not long to wait. The day after my advertisement was published a steady stream of decayed travellers appeared, all anxious to carry the 'attractive side-line' as advertised. All wanted a small salary, the majority wanted a small advance on account. All were told the same tale: no salary to start with, commission only if results justified it, salary would follow. All were given a sample with price-list. Their commission was lavish, 20%, if I remember aright.

My dilapidated army set out and again I sat down to wait results. After a few days orders began to arrive. Mr. Young himself booked a few, others came from the decayed gentry, brought up to the office personally and being accompanied invariably by the request for a small advance; and so the business grew. I decided to spread out and to take a warehouse, to buy in larger bulk and store and dispatch myself. The basement of a tumbledown house on the south bank was obtained for a small rental. I wanted Mr. Young to take charge of the warehouse, but Mr. Young, while agreeing, insisted on having a boy to help him pack and handle the goods.

So there and then I inserted an advertisement in an evening paper,—'Strong boy wanted to help in warehouse.' The day after the advertisement appeared I got out at Mark Lane Station and, as I approached Water Lane, was surprised to see what appeared to be a dot with two policemen trying to restore order. The whole of Water Lane, up to its juncture with Mark Lane, was one seething mass of 'strong boys' come from all parts of the land to 'help in warehouse'. I slipped into the office by a back entrance, pushed my way through the 'strong boys' who blocked the passage and banged and pushed at the locked door. It was opened to me by a white-faced, thoroughly terrified Mr. Young. We engaged the boy at the head of the queue, put a large notice on the door 'Job filled', locked the door and remained in a state of siege. For days after, Strong Boys hung around the Water Lane office. Glowering and muttering Strong Boys banged at the locked door and threatened to break in. Strong Boys waylaid us in the passages and in the streets as we scuttled in and out.

The business began to boom. We sold soap to hotels, to boarding houses, to ships' chandiers and to street barrows. It was very cheap at 18/- per cwt., but it was also very bad, mostly soda; the fatty acid content (the test of good soap) was ridiculously small. 'Water held together by caustic soda' was how an angry customer described it! But what could they expect at the price? One day a very vulgar and ferociously angry woman banged her way into the office. She carried a small infant, pulled its clothes over its head and thrust a raw and inflamed posterior into my face. The poor child looked like a boiled lobster. The wretched woman had washed the infant in a strong solution of 'Baird's Speedy Cleaner'. I calmed her down and pointed out that the Speedy Cleaner was a powerful scouring soap for floors and ship decks, and not a toilet soap for infants.

One day Young came back from his round full of excitement with a cake of soap labelled 'Hutchinson's Rapid Washer'. Hutchinson had come in on the barrow trade and was cutting prices, selling for 16/- a cwt. I got on the telephone and he agreed to call and see me. He proved to be a hearty, jovial young Irishman.[12] We got on well together and came to the conclusion that we should join forces. We met that night and dined together at the Cafe Royal. We sat long into the night drinking old brandy and settling the last details of our merger. I felt ill when he saw me off at Leicester Square Tube Station. Next morning I had a high temperature and a terrific cold. I had left my old lodgings and was staying in a cheap residential hotel (Bed and breakfast, full board Sunday, 30/-). My bedroom was a converted conservatory and bitterly cold. I got rapidly worse. Hutchinson appeared with a bottle of Eau de Cologne and was thoroughly alarmed at my state. The doctor was called in

12 Oliver George Hutchinson (1891–1944) was from Belfast. He had actually met Baird before the war when they were both apprentices with the Argyll Motor Company.*

and I got steadily worse. He became concerned and told me that I must get out of London at once or he would not answer for my recovery.

Mephy was in Hastings and next day I packed my bag and set off to join him. The business had prospered and I had fulfilled a long held ambition by forming it into a Limited Company with £2,000 authorized capital.[13] My co-directors, two young business men to whom Pound had introduced me, bought out my shares, leaving me with a sum of roughly £200.

13 The company did little further business and was wound up in March 1928.*

Chapter Four

Coughing, choking and spluttering, and so thin as to be almost transparent, I arrived at Hastings station, assets totalling approximately £200, prospects nothing. Mephy was waiting for me at the station and had arranged for me to share his lodgings. Fortunately, the weather was perfect and it was late spring. I began to recover and it can be said that Hastings saved my life. Then the problem of money arose; my funds were getting low, what was to be done? I must invent something. I first thought of a safety razor made entirely of glass so that it would not rust or tarnish. The blade also was to be made of glass. The glass blade was not a success and after cutting myself rather badly I decided to try pneumatic soles, so that people could walk with the same advantage that a car gains from its pneumatic tyres. I got a pair of very large boots, and put inside them two partially inflated balloons, and then very carefully inserted my feet, laced up the boots and set off on a short trial run. I walked a hundred yards in a succession of drunken and uncontrollable lurches followed by a few delighted urchins, till the demonstration was brought to an end by one of my tyres bursting.

More thought was needed. I went for a long walk over the cliffs to Fairlight Glen, and my mind went back to my early work on television. Might there not be something in it now? My difficulty then had been to find a means of amplifying the infinitesimally small current from the selenium cell. Such an amplifier was now available, thanks to Fleming and De Forest. Why not try again? The more I thought of it the easier it seemed. I thought out a complete system and returned to Walton Crescent[1] filled with an influx of new life and hope. Over the raisin pudding I broke the news to Mephy.

'Well, sir, you will be pleased to hear that I have invented a means of seeing by wireless'. 'Oh,' said Mephy, 'I hope that doesn't mean you are going to become one of those wireless nitwits. Far better keep to soap. You can't afford to play about you know'.

However he was very helpful and operations were started by the purchase of a tea chest, an old hat box, some darning needles and a bullseye lens from

1 This was almost certainly 21 Linton Crescent, the home of Mr and Mrs Charles Wheatley, where Baird and Mephy are known to have boarded.*

Baird and Mephy Robertson on the seafront at Hastings, soon after Baird's arrival.

the local shop, also a plentiful supply of sealing wax and secotine.[2] The contraption grew and filled my bedroom; electric batteries were added to it. Wireless valves and transformers and neon lamps appeared and at last to my great joy I was able to show the shadow of a little cross transmitted over a few feet.

The apparatus was very simple, indeed its simplicity saved it. A circular disc of cardboard had been cut out of a hat box, and two spirals of holes had been pierced in it with the sharp end of a pair of scissors; a darning needle formed the spindle and by means of bobbins this could be revolved; on one side of the disc a powerful electric lamp shone through the bullseye lens upon a little cardboard cross and cast a shadow on the discs. On one side of this revolving disc another disc, which had been cut out of tin plate (with the same scissors) and had a great number of little serrations round its edges, was mounted on the spindle of a little electric fan motor which revolved it at a great speed, and was arranged in the path of the light. On the other side of the cardboard disc was a selenium cell; the interrupted light falling on the cell generated a current which was sent to a neon lamp fixed behind the same disc but at the opposite edge from the selenium cell. The cell was connected through an amplifier to the lamp. The lamp glowed when the cell was

2 Secotine was a brand of fish glue.

Baird with early apparatus at 21 Linton Crescent, Hastings. (Royal Television Society)

illuminated and went out when it was in the shade, so that when the apparatus revolved it was possible to see on one half of the disc the shadow of the cross on the other half, a distance of two feet.

I was much elated. I was on the right track. A start had been made. But my money was going so I gave a demonstration to the press hoping to attract capital. The whole thing was, however, too embryonic, but I managed to get a puff in the *Daily News* and by a fortunate chance a far-sighted friend of my father saw it and strongly advised him that my work might well develop into something of world-wide importance. This so impressed the old man that he sent me £50 although I had not asked him for anything. Thus I was able to ease a certain tension which had arisen in my digs, due to my using my bedroom as a laboratory, by removing my apparatus to a small room above a shop in the Queen's Arcade at Hastings. For this I paid 5/- per week rent.

Here I spent many happy hours and came as near to death as I am ever likely to come and survive. The plant grew until it became a nightmare cobweb of wires and batteries, and little lamp bulbs and whirling discs, but the results were far better. I could transmit shadows of letters and simple outlines from one machine to another. Once again money began to run low. I advertised in *The Times*.[3]

3 27 June 1923.

'Seeing by Wireless—Inventor of Apparatus wishes to hear from someone who will assist (not financially) in making working model. Write Box ...etc.'

I thought it better not to ask directly for money and I think this was wise; anyhow my advertisement got two good bites. One came from Mr. Odhams the chairman of Odhams Press and the other from Mr. Will Day, a man with a good going wireless and cinema business and well known in cinema circles. In addition I got in touch with William Le Queux,[4] the novelist, who lived in Hastings and called several times to see my work and also wrote several articles about it for the *Radio Times* and other journals. I thought I would form a small company with William Le Queux, Odhams and Day. Odhams sent down to Hastings two experts; a man named F.H. Robinson, the editor of *Broadcasting*,[5] an Odhams publication, and also Captain A.G.D. West[6] who was then chief Research Engineer with the B.B.C. Many years later, he was to join my company. Both were impressed favourably, but both thought that I had a long way to go and could see no practical use for a device that could only send shadows.

Mr. Odhams, however, when I went to see him in London was very charming, gave me tea and entertained me with a respect and consideration which were balm to the soul of a struggling inventor accustomed to being regarded as a dangerous crank.

'Well now, Mr. Odhams,' I said, 'what kind of demonstration would convince you?'

'If you could put a machine' he said, 'in the room next door and sit someone in front of it, and then on the screen of a machine in this room show his face, not a shadow but a face, then I am certain you would get all the money you want. I am anxious to help,' he added, 'and I have discussed this with West and Robinson, but what can we do with a device which can only send shadows?'

William Le Queux was willing and eager to help, but unfortunately all his money was tied up in some investments in Switzerland. Robinson was the editor of *The Cinema* and published in it an article describing what he had seen. This saved the ship. It was read by Will Day and without debate or delay he bought a one third interest for £200. His solicitor—an ancient and

4 William Le Queux (1864–1927) was a writer of best-selling spy stories, many of which had a scientific flavour, for example, 'The Green Ray'.

5 The magazine's correct title was *The Broadcaster*.*

6 Capt. Albert G.D. West (1898-1949) had served as a wireless officer in World War I and then had a brilliant undergraduate career at Cambridge. He spent a year working at the Cavendish Laboratory under Sir Ernest Rutherford before joining the B.B.C. West later became technical director of Baird Television Ltd. (See chapter 9).*

crafty gentleman in a dirty collar—made me sign a document whereby I afterwards found I had bound myself to pay all expenses in developing the invention and the costs of taking out patents in every country in the world. Fortunately the document was so badly drawn up that it was found later to be completely illegal. I did not read it at the time; I would indeed have signed away my immortal soul for £200 and I was not going to quibble over the terms of a legal document.[7]

I hurried back to Hastings and Mephy and I dined at Molinari's to celebrate the occasion. The next day I bought several hundred flash lamp batteries and began to realize my dream of a 2,000 volt power supply, by joining sufficient dry batteries end to end—a formidable task. Some days later I had finished this and was connecting the supply to some part of the cobweb of wiring when my attention wandered and I received the full force of the 2,000 volts through my two hands. It was amply sufficient to cause death, but I was lucky, for a few seconds I was twisted into a knot in helpless agony and then fortunately fell over backwards, breaking the circuit and saving my life. But I shall never forget the agony of those few seconds. Electrocution must be a terrible death. The noise of my fall and the flash of light collected a small crowd and next day the papers came out with a lurid story—'Inventor pinned to the ground by short circuit'. 'Serious explosion in Hastings Laboratory'.

Mr. Twigg,[8] from whom I rented the laboratory, sent me a sharp note saying that my experiments, which were liable to damage his property, must cease forthwith, or I must instantly vacate his premises. I ignored this letter entirely and one afternoon, while working in my laboratory, where I could be seen by anyone standing in the Arcade, I was astonished and very much annoyed to find Mr. Twigg standing there, waving his arms and shouting at me.

'What are you doing there? I told you I could have no further experiments carried out in my premises. You must stop this nonsense at once'.

I was very angry and marched downstairs to put the old gentleman in his place. 'Excuse me, Mr. Twigg, but this is scarcely the way to carry on business; I am paying you rent for these premises and I have a perfect right to use them without you standing there bawling and shouting at me'.

7 The partnership between Baird and Day was an uneasy one. Although Baird kept Day well informed about the details of his progress, Day became impatient and worried about his investment. The letters exchanged between the two men are now in the Hastings Museum and Art Gallery.

8 Baird had a habit of giving wrong names to people he disliked. 'Mr. Twigg' was his name for Alderman Ben Went Tree, who had been mayor of Hastings four times. Upon his death in 1927, Mr. Tree left money in a trust fund for the Hastings Museum. In 1999, that fund helped the museum to acquire the original letters between Baird and Wilfred Day.*

By this time a small crowd had collected. I did not wish a scene so I turned my back on him in a dignified fashion and marched off but was rather astonished by a roar of laughter from the crowd. A few minutes later I discovered that in thrusting my hands violently into my trouser pockets, I had strained this dilapidated garment and torn a large rent in the seat. Mr. Twigg, however, had his way; a day or two later I received a letter from his solicitor instructing me that I must vacate his premises. This, coupled with Will Day's urgent advice decided me to leave Hastings and transfer my laboratory to London. Will Day had found suitable premises in a little attic at 22 Frith Street, and it was to this I moved my apparatus.[9]

Some years later the Hastings town council affixed a little tablet above the entrance to the attic over Mr. Twigg's shop which reads:

'Queen's Arcade, Hastings.
Television first demonstrated by John Logie Baird from
experiments started here in 1924.'

I was invited to the unveiling on 7th November 1929 which was quite a ceremony. Sir Ambrose Fleming, who was invited but unable to attend, sent a very nice letter to the Hastings Corporation:

> 'I regret very much that another important engagement at the Institution of Electrical Engineers tonight prevents me from accepting the kind invitation of the mayor of Hastings to be present at the interesting ceremony of the unveiling of a plaque commemorating the historic and epoch-making work of Mr. Baird. This plaque will be a perpetual reminder that Mr. Baird was the first to effect practical television and to inaugurate a new departure in electrical technique which will have immense development in present and future years.'

Arriving in London, I took lodgings in Ealing and had the top floor front. I paid, I think, 8/- for the room and cooked my own food on a gas ring. The room was comfortable and quiet. On the wall was a framed poem:—

> 'Short was the traveller's stay, She came but as a guest,
> She tasted life then fled away, To everlasting rest.'
> Elizabeth Brown passed away aged three months—

Further along the wall was a photograph of an infant in a cot, evidently the dead body of little Elizabeth Brown. On the table were a number of books, Dickens, Silas Hocking and Annie Swan, also a book of press cuttings from *Tit Bits and Answers* headed 'Jokes and Teasers from Various Columns'.

9 The move from Hastings to London took place in early November, 1924.*

The first night I stayed there the door handle of the bedroom was very slowly and quietly turned, and the door began to open. I watched spell-bound. The door opened about two inches and then stopped, there was the sound of someone moving stealthily away and then complete silence. Nothing more happened.

Every night the same phenomenon occurred. I found at last that it was the landlady's little boy who slept next door and suffered from night fears. He wanted to have the door open for company. Every night, for all the time I stayed there, this pathetic little ceremony took place.

Mr. Gray, the General Manager of the Marconi Company, had once lived next door to us at a house called 'Carisbrook' in Helensburgh. So one day I thought I would call and see if I could get him to take an interest in what I was doing. I called at Marconi House, sent in my name, 'Mr. Baird from Helensburgh' and after half an hour in the waiting room was shown into a large office where an elderly man sat behind a large, important looking desk.

I said, 'Good morning', 'Good morning', said Mr. Gray. 'Are you interested in television?' said I. 'Not in the very slightest degree, no interest whatsoever', said Mr. Gray.

His disclaimer was as emphatic and disapproving as if I had asked him if he was interested in brothels.

'I am sorry to have wasted your time. Good-morning', I said and immediately walked out in high dudgeon.

This episode shows the general attitude to television in 1925. It was regarded as a wildcat myth, something on a par with the Perpetual Motion Machine. Television could never be realised unless some hitherto undreamt of discoveries were made, and nothing of the sort was in sight. That was the view held by the Marconi experts and the experts and men of science generally. The view of the press and the public was somewhat similar, and is illustrated by another episode which took place shortly after my visit to Marconi's.

I thought if I could get a story in the press I might attract someone with capital; with this end in view I called at the office of the *Daily Express* and asked to see the Editor. After a short delay I was ushered into a small room and the Editor (at least I thought it was the Editor) came hurrying to see me.

'Are you interested in a machine for television—seeing by wireless?' I said.

'Seeing by wireless?' said the 'Editor', a little taken aback.

'Oh yes,' said I, 'an apparatus that will let you see the people who are being broadcast by the B.B.C. or speaking on the telephone.'

'Astounding,' said the gentleman, 'I am very busy at a meeting, but I will get one of my colleagues to take the story, very interesting,' and he vanished

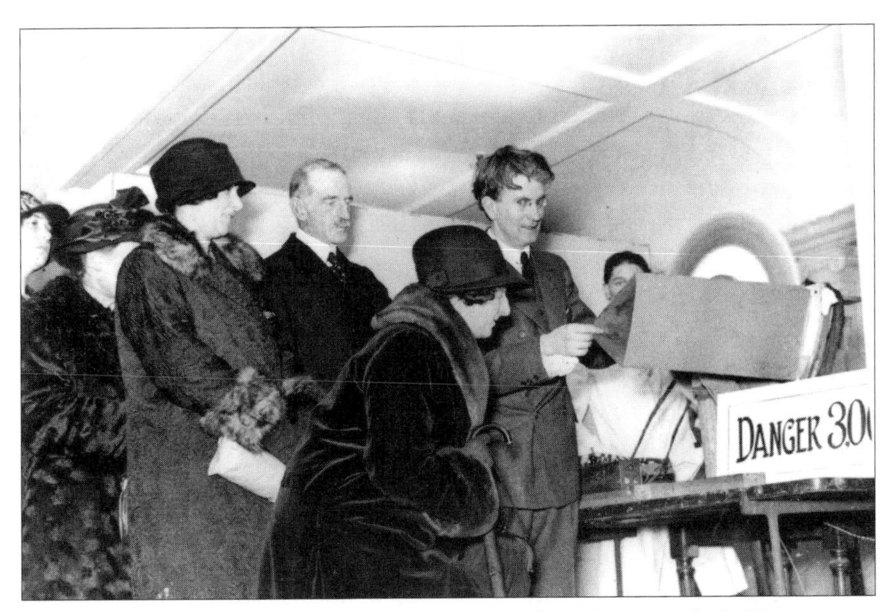

Demonstrating primitive television at Selfridge's in March 1925.
(Royal Television Society)

out of the door. In a few minutes a large brawny individual came in, listened sympathetically and with great interest to my tale, assured me that it was a first call story and advised me to be sure and get the copy of next day's *Express*, where I would get a first class show on the front page.

And so with a cordial handshake he saw me off the premises.

Nothing whatever appeared in the *Express*, and it was only some years after that I got the inside story from the brawny individual himself. The day I called he was sitting in the press room when one of the assistant editors came running in.

'For God's sake, Jackson, go down to the reception room and get rid of a lunatic who is there. He says he's got a machine for seeing by wireless. Watch him carefully, he may have a razor hidden.'

I continued to work away in my Frith Street attic transmitting crude outlines of letters and figures and anxiously watching the cash getting less and less. One day I had two visitors; one was Mr. Gordon Selfridge, junior, the other[10] had visited me in Hastings and was interested in my work. He had mentioned it to Selfridge and Selfridge, who was on the lookout for an attraction for his Birthday Week celebrations, had thought that television would be a startling exhibit. I was offered twenty pounds a week for three weeks to give three shows a day to the public in Selfridge's store. I accepted the offer and spent a very trying three weeks demonstrating to long queues of

10 The other visitor was Count Anthony de Bosdari, a friend of Selfridge.*

spectators, most of them ordinary shoppers, but also a number of scientists who had come specially to see the show. By looking down a funnel arrangement they were able to see outlines of shapes transmitted only a few yards by a crude wireless transmitter. The strain of giving three shows a day on this rickety apparatus was too much for me and I was ill for several weeks after it. The apparatus went back to Frith Street and with a little more money to go on with, the research continued.

It was an anxious time. The money problem became pressing and it occurred to me in desperation to advertise for a company promoter. A number turned up. These gentlemen looked at my apparatus with lack-lustre eyes and departed, all except one, a Mr. Brooks. He had the proper spirit and assured me it was the finest proposition he had ever had placed before him, and all he wanted was an advance of £25 for his expenses and my fortune was made. His scheme was to send a circular letter to all the doctors on the register explaining the wonderful possibilities of the invention and enclosing a postcard, having written on it, 'If you are interested please return this postcard and my representative will call'. I was not prepared to pay Mr. Brooks £25, but we went together and had the letters printed. We then went together and posted them to the number of 3,000. Out of this 3,000, six replies were received. Mr. Brooks called on these six and collected £75. The expenses

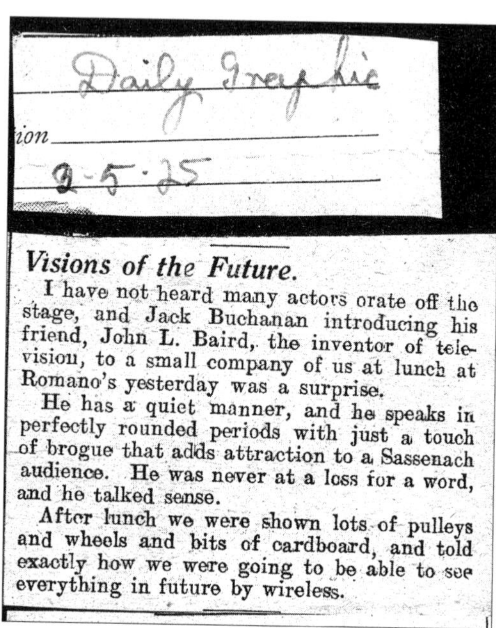
Daily Graphic

ion

2-5-25

Visions of the Future.

I have not heard many actors orate off the stage, and Jack Buchanan introducing his friend, John L. Baird, the inventor of television, to a small company of us at lunch at Romano's yesterday was a surprise.

He has a quiet manner, and he speaks in perfectly rounded periods with just a touch of brogue that adds attraction to a Sassenach audience. He was never at a loss for a word, and he talked sense.

After lunch we were shown lots of pulleys and wheels and bits of cardboard, and told exactly how we were going to be able to see everything in future by wireless.

Shortly after the Selfridge's demonstration, Jack Buchanan, by now a theatrical star, held a luncheon to introduce Baird and television to the press. This slightly sceptical report is taken from Baird's scrap-book.

he claimed amounted to well over this figure and he wished to retain the whole amount. However, we finally settled for £25 and two double whiskies. Fortunately in addition, two of my cousins, the Inglis's, put up £500, so Television Limited[11] was in funds.

There were other bright lights in adversity. The heads of big business firms are not all lacking in imagination and enterprise. Shortly after the Selfridge show a man called at Frith Street. He seemed pleasant and said he represented Hart's Accumulators. Did I want any batteries? I did very badly and discussed the matter with him. He told me what I needed would cost about £200. 1 told him that the most I could spend was about £10, and he went off.

A few days later I was astounded to get a letter from the managing director of the Hart Company saying that the company was desirous of encouraging my pioneer work, and had decided to make me a present of £200 worth of batteries. It was a bright spot in the darkness of anxious days.

Shortly after this the General Electric Company gave me a present of £200 worth of valves. These gifts were extremely useful. The enterprise of the donors was rewarded. We subsequently bought thousands of pounds worth of valves and batteries from them. But for hard-headed business men to give £200 worth of goods to a dilapidated and penniless crank in a garret is a phenomenon worth recording.

In this country my chief potential rival was Dr. E.E. Fournier D'Albe, the inventor of the Optophone, a remarkable and clever device by which the blind can read ordinary print. He was working feverishly on television, his idea being to send out every spot of the picture on a different frequency so as to avoid the difficulty of synchronism, which he considered insuperable. He wrote an article in *Nature* in which he proved to his own satisfaction and the evident satisfaction of the scientific world that this was so. By the time the article appeared I had actually shown television and overcome the synchronism problem and was able to point out the fallacy upon which his conclusions were based.

Briefly speaking, Fournier D'Albe had made the mistake of thinking the slightest difference in speed or position between receiving the transmitting apparatus would scramble the picture; whereas all it did was to give a slight movement to the picture as a whole. Misled by this calculation, which was generally accepted at the time by the scientific world, he set off on an impossible complicated scheme. Each picture point was to be sent out on a different wavelength and the whole picture to be sent simultaneously. The scheme was quite impractical.

11 This company, the world's first television company, had been registered on 11 June 1925. The directors were Baird and Will Day.*

The ideas regarding television in 1925 are surprising today when television is taken as a matter of fact, and the method by which it is accomplished is also now regarded as the obvious method. In 1925 it was not so. In fact it was the very reverse.

Not only Dr. Fournier D'Albe but a great number of scientists insisted that television could not be accomplished on the principle which I had adopted. I was trying to get television by dividing the picture into a series of little sections of light and darkness and sending these in very rapid succession. That is the principle in general use today, whereas the prevailing school of thought considered that some means must be discovered (it had not been discovered yet) whereby the whole picture could be sent simultaneously.

Fournier D'Albe, however, was right in recognising the other barrier to television by my method; that was the question of light. He pointed out quite accurately that in the transmission of silhouettes the whole light from the light source fell straight into the photocell. This light could be anything from hundreds to thousands of candle power and the sending of shadows was therefore easy. But where the human face was to be transmitted, the face itself had to reflect the light and the light thrown out from the human face, even when the person was sitting under the illumination of an arc lamp, was infinitesimal.

Another possible rival, A.A.Campbell Swinton,[12] whose ideas on television were thoroughly sound had (perhaps fortunately for me) abandoned his work.

In the U.S.A., Jenkins[13] was working with a device using a complex circular twisted prismatic disc, but he was baulked, chiefly I think, by the insensitivity of the photo-cells he used and showed only shadows. Thus in the U.S.A. the first television demonstration was not given by Jenkins, but by the American Telegraph and Telephone Company and that was over fourteen months after my demonstration in January 1926.

Light, how to provide more light was the most serious problem with which I was faced. The photoelectric cells then available were quite irresponsive to the light given by my apparatus. In my efforts to increase this I built enormous discs. One was as big as eight foot in diameter and had fitted round it spirals of bigger and bigger lenses, until I got to using lenses eight inches in

12 Alan Archibald Campbell Swinton was a Scottish physicist who in 1911 had proposed an entire system of television based on cathode ray tubes. This was a brilliant theoretical prophecy but as late as 1924 Swinton stated that the practical development of electronic television would be 'scarcely worth anyone's while to pursue it'. Baird read and took note of this statement.*

13 Charles Frances Jenkins (1867-1934) did much work on phototelegraphy but in the area of television he never got beyond the sending of shadows.

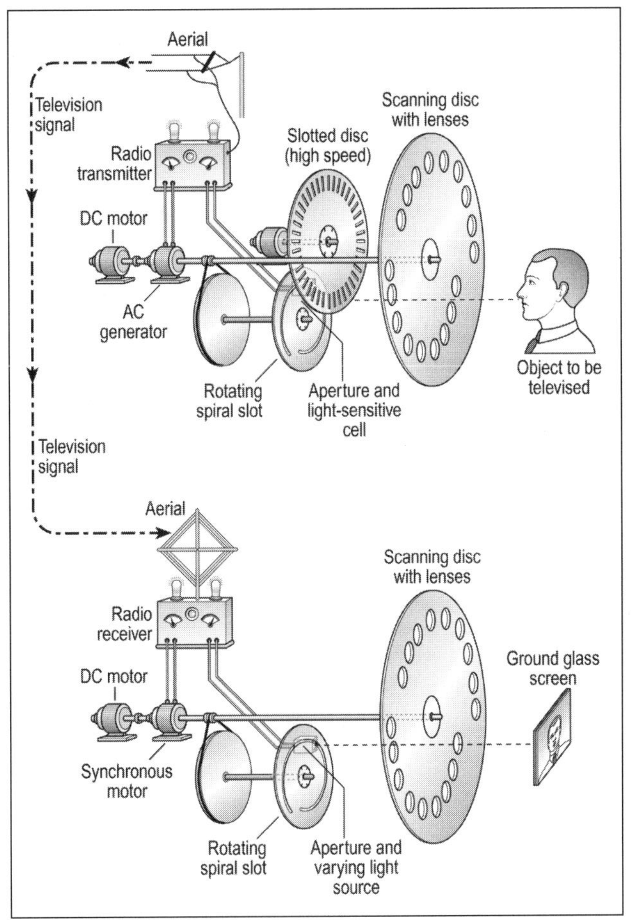

Basic principle of mechanical television, from an article by Baird in The Journal of Scientific Instruments, *January 1927, redrawn by Robert Britton (National Museum of Scotland).*

diameter. Light, light, more light: I soon reached a limit in this direction, my enormous wheels almost filled the little laboratory and as they had to revolve at an absolute minimum of 150 revolutions per minute, they were distinctly dangerous. The discs were made in sizes up to five feet in thick cardboard, and beyond that size I used three-ply wood. On more than one occasion lenses broke loose, striking the walls or roof like bomb shells. The apparatus would then get out of balance and jump from one side of the laboratory to the other until it was stopped or the disc tore itself to pieces. I had some exciting moments.

In spite of every effort however, I could not get anything like enough light to operate the photoelectric cells available and I decided to try either to make a new cell or find some way of using the sensitive selenium cell. Two devices sensitive to light were known, the selenium cell and the photoelectric cell. The photoelectric cell of those days was so extremely insensitive to light that no detectable signals could be got from it, except by shining a powerful light directly into it. It could be used to show the difference between total darkness and the light from a powerful arc lamp, so that it was possible by interposing simple shapes in the path of an arc lamp beam, to send their shadows; but to use it for true television where all the light available would be relatively infinitesimal light thrown back from, say, a human face, was utterly out of the question.

The selenium cell was enormously more sensitive, but it had what all writers on the subject agreed was an insurmountable objection to its use—a time lag; that is it took some little time to respond to light.

I made a number of efforts to increase the sensitivity of the photo-electric cells and to find other materials which would give greater reactions to light. The light sensitivity of the human eye, according to Eldridge, Green and certain others, resides in a purple fluid found in the retina of the eye, and called the visual purple.

I decided to make an experimental cell using this substance, and called at the Charing Cross Ophthalmic Hospital, and asked to see the chief surgeon. I told him I wanted an eye for some research work I was doing on visual purple. He thought I was a doctor and was very helpful.

'You've come at an appropriate time', he said, 'I am just taking out an eye, and will let you have it, if you will take a seat until the operation is over.'

I was handed an eye wrapped in cotton wool—a gruesome object. I made a crude effort to dissect this with a razor, but gave it up and threw the whole mess into the canal. My efforts to produce a sensitive cell without time lag proving abortive, I decided to try selenium cells and see what could be done—if anything—to overcome the time lag. The first thing I tried was to use interrupted light, by passing the light rays through a serrated disc, which acted as a light chopper. The time lag did not enter into the matter. The cell had to distinguish only between interruptions and no interruptions. With this I could use selenium but the light chopper split the picture into crude bars, so nothing could be sent but coarse outlines. I discarded the chopper and concentrated on the problem of overcoming time lag.

I used, as the object for my experimental transmission, a ventriloquist's dummy's head. This came out on the screen as a streaky blob. What was happening was this: When the light fell on the cell, the current, instead of jumping instantly to its full value, rose slowly and continued rising as long as the light fell on it. Then when the light was cut off the current did not stop

Baird with his apparatus at the Science Museum. (Royal Television Society)

instantly, but only stopped increasing and began falling, taking an appreciable time to get to zero. While watching this effect, it occurred to me that it could be cured or mitigated if I superimposed a curve representing the rate of change of the current with time upon the curve of current with time.

By putting a transformer in the circuit I could, in effect, accomplish this. The moment the light fell upon the cell there would be a change from no current to current. And although the current would be small the rate of change would be great; again at the time when current changed from increasing to decreasing, the rate of change would be maximum, so that I would get a big up kick and a big down kick when required.[14] My amplifier was a D.C. battery coupled amplifier (and a source of infinite worry). Now I deciued to build a second amplifier, battery coupled but with one transformer coupled stage, so that one amplifier could give me the time/current curve, and the second the time/rate of change of current curve. I would then mix the two until the time lag was corrected. And this I proceeded to do. This, that and the other thing went wrong, but I saw enough to realize I was on the right track.

Funds were going down, the situation was becoming desperate and we were down to our last £30 when at last, one Friday in the first week of

14 This is an application of Faraday's law of induction, which Baird knew about from his studies at the Royal Technical College.

October 1925, everything functioned properly. The image of the dummy's head formed itself on the screen with what appeared to me almost unbelievable clarity. I had got it! I could scarcely believe my eyes, and felt myself shaking with excitement.

I ran down the little flight of stairs to Mr. Cross's office and seized by the arm his office boy William Taynton, hauled him upstairs and put him in front of the transmitter. I then went to the receiver only to find the screen a blank. William did not like the lights and the whirring discs and had withdrawn out of range. I gave him 2/6 and pushed his head into position. This time he came through and on the screen I saw the flickering, but clearly recognisable, image of William's face—the first face seen by television—and he had to be bribed with 2/6 for the privilege of achieving this distinction.

The original apparatus and the dummy's head are now in the Science Museum at South Kensington.[15]

15 The apparatus is now at the National Museum of Photography, Film and Television in Bradford.

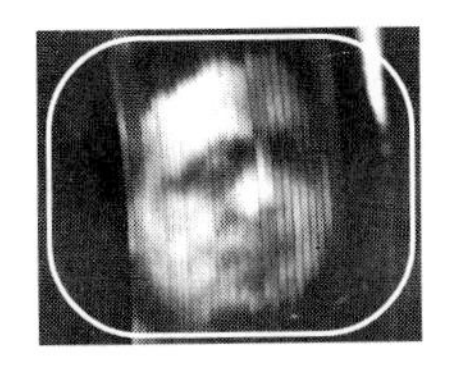

Chapter Five

Television had been achieved. I was definitely able to transmit the living image and it was the first time it had been done. But how to convince the sceptical, hide-bound, select and exclusive scientific world? Would they admit that a wretched nonentity working with soap boxes in a garret had done something which many of them had stated was impossible?

I wanted to show my results to the world, to nail down at once that I was first. I was extremely nervous in case, while I waited, someone else achieved television and gave a show before I did. Hutchinson did not want to show it. He was terrified that someone would copy my work and particularly frightened (with very good cause) that the big wireless concerns would be given an impetus to take up television research and use my work as a guide.

However we compromised by inviting the members of the Royal Institution to a demonstration and inviting only *The Times* to represent the Press. This, we felt, would give dignity and importance to the demonstration. On the appointed evening, Friday 27th January 1926,[1] over 40 members of the Institution turned up, all in full evening dress, mostly distinguished scientists but with a sprinkling of ladies. This gorgeous gathering found that they were expected to climb three flights of narrow stone stairs, and then to stand in a narrow draughty passage, while batches of six at a time were brought into the two tiny attic rooms which formed my laboratory.

In one room was a large whirling disc, a most dangerous device, had they known it, liable to burst at any minute and hop round the room with showers of broken glass. However, all went well except for two small incidents. One of the visitors who was being transmitted had a long white beard, part of which blew into the wheel. Fortunately, he escaped with the loss of a certain amount of hair. He was a thorough sportsman and took the accident in good part and insisted on continuing the experiment and having his face transmitted. The whole assembly were given an opportunity to be televised and I was certainly gratified by the interest and enthusiasm. The audience were for the most part men of vision and realized that in these tiny flickering images they

1 News of Baird's demonstration appeared in *The Times* on Thursday 28th January but the demonstration itself had taken place on the evening of Tuesday 26th January.

were witnessing the birth of a great industry. One, who had made a study of television and carried out many experiments himself, was heard to remark, 'Baird has got it. The rest is merely a matter of £. s. d.' These were great days.

An account of the demonstration was published in *The Times* the next day. It brought an army of pressmen to 22, Frith Street in search of stories.

Then followed continual demonstrations to the scientific and daily press, and to interested scientists. Among these was Dr. Alexander Russell who, as a past president of the General Electric Company and the Principal of Faraday House, spoke with authority; he wrote:—

> '...Even the most optimistic of scientific men had begun to think that it would be many years before the first glimmering of a practical method would be developed. We were therefore agreeably surprised on making a visit to Mr. J.L. Baird at Motograph House[2] ...to find that he had installed there a transmitter and a receiver which prove that he has made great progress in solving the problem ...This is the first time we have seen real television, and, so far as we know, Mr. Baird is the first to have accomplished this feat... Those of us who remember the advent of the telephone in 1876, and remember also how little its importance was then realised, will hesitate to criticise this new invention'. (*Nature,* July 3rd 1926).

Similar accounts by other eyewitnesses appeared in the other scientific journals. I knew that I had stolen a march upon the scientific world and that every attempt would be made to ignore my existence, to cast doubts on the authenticity of my demonstrations and to use every method of implication and innuendo to belittle my work. Either it was not television, or it had been done before and in any case it was of no consequence, I was a vulgar and ignorant fellow of whom no one had ever heard, and I could not be taken seriously. The fact remains, however, that I was showing television and no one else was able to do so. I took full advantage of this and gave continual demonstrations to the press and to any scientist who cared to come, so that the press of 1926 is filled with accounts of these shows. These demonstrations stood alone; neither in U.S.A. nor in Germany nor elsewhere were any demonstrations given; nevertheless, even to this day persons connected with rival trade concerns ignore this altogether and deal with the first demonstration of television by such little statements as 'about 1926 many experimenters

2 In February 1926 Television Ltd. had moved from 22 Frith Street to more spacious premises at Motograph House, in St Martin's Lane.

'These were great days'. Hutchinson and Baird with Sir Oliver Lodge. (Royal Television Society)

were transmitting television images'. The truth was that until April 1927, over a year later than my first show, I was the only person to show television.

For fourteen months from our first demonstration we had a complete monopoly, then in 1927 the American Telegraph and Telephone Company staged a spectacular show and heralded it as 'Television at last', entirely ignoring my work. Of this demonstration Dr. Dauvillier, a distinguished French scientist and television expert, wrote:[3]

I write perhaps somewhat bitterly and egotistically about this matter, but even after the lapse of years, and at an age where such things should not matter, I feel again my anger against the jealous malice which would willingly, contrary to all justice and all evidence, have brushed my work aside and distorted the facts by every mean trick of omission, innuendo and misrepresentation. They did not however find me easy to crush; years of fierce struggle to keep alive had certainly taught me to fight and I kept kicking and

3 A blank space appears in the typescript at this point; Baird had meant to insert part of Dauvillier's article which had appeared in a French technical journal in January 1928. Dauvillier had commented that A.T.& T. had used the Baird system 'without permission'.*

shouting, sometimes (I am afraid) paying little attention to dignity or reticence in the publicity methods employed.

In spite of demonstrations to every newspaper from *The Times* to *Tit-Bits*, and to everyone who was willing to come, from the office boy to the Prime Minister, the atmosphere of supercilious aloofness was maintained by the B.B.C. and by many in the most select scientific circles, particularly by those connected with rival trade interests, but when at length a committee of Members of Parliament advised by the experts of the Post Office and B.B.C. investigated my invention and reported that it was a 'Notable scientific achievement', it silenced all hints of trickery and doubt. Some of the larger-minded scientists admitted their misplaced scepticism, among these being Campbell Swinton, who with a gesture that does him infinite credit wrote to *The Times* that television had arrived and he had witnessed it.

Sir John Reith tells how at that time, sitting in the Athenaeum, he heard the booming voice of Campbell Swinton say 'I have been converted, I have been converted'. Reith thought at first that C.S. had been the victim of a religious revival, but C.S. was merely telling him that he had seen a demonstration and had been converted to a belief that my work was in fact genuine and that television had arrived.

Looking back on these days I am not surprised at this struggle for recognition. The impact on the scientific world of an utterly undignified young inventor claiming to see through brick walls and heralded by headlines in the daily press, such as 'Magic in a Garret' and 'Young Scotsman's Magic Eye', were calculated to induce the most acute hostility and scepticism.

Fournier D'Albe and Campbell Swinton had some excuse for their first unbelief as they had not then seen a demonstration. But others even when they saw our results suspected trickery. I remember being called away in the middle of a demonstration to a distinguished scientist. I came back suddenly and was surprised to find this venerable old gentleman crawling about under the apparatus. He was a little embarrassed, but pointed out that as he had to make a report it was his duty to satisfy himself that there was no trickery.

I was accused of hiding a boy in a box behind the receiver and all sorts of tricks. These accusations were usually made by people who had never seen a demonstration and made usually in newspaper articles in the form of innuendo and implication. They were killed by repeated demonstration. The critics then changed their ground to, 'it is of no use', and finally, as a last resort, 'Anyone could have done it'.

The picture was made up of 30 strips. I had found this to be the minimum necessary to transmit a clearly recognisable image of the human face. To decide the shape of the picture most suitable to take in the face without waste

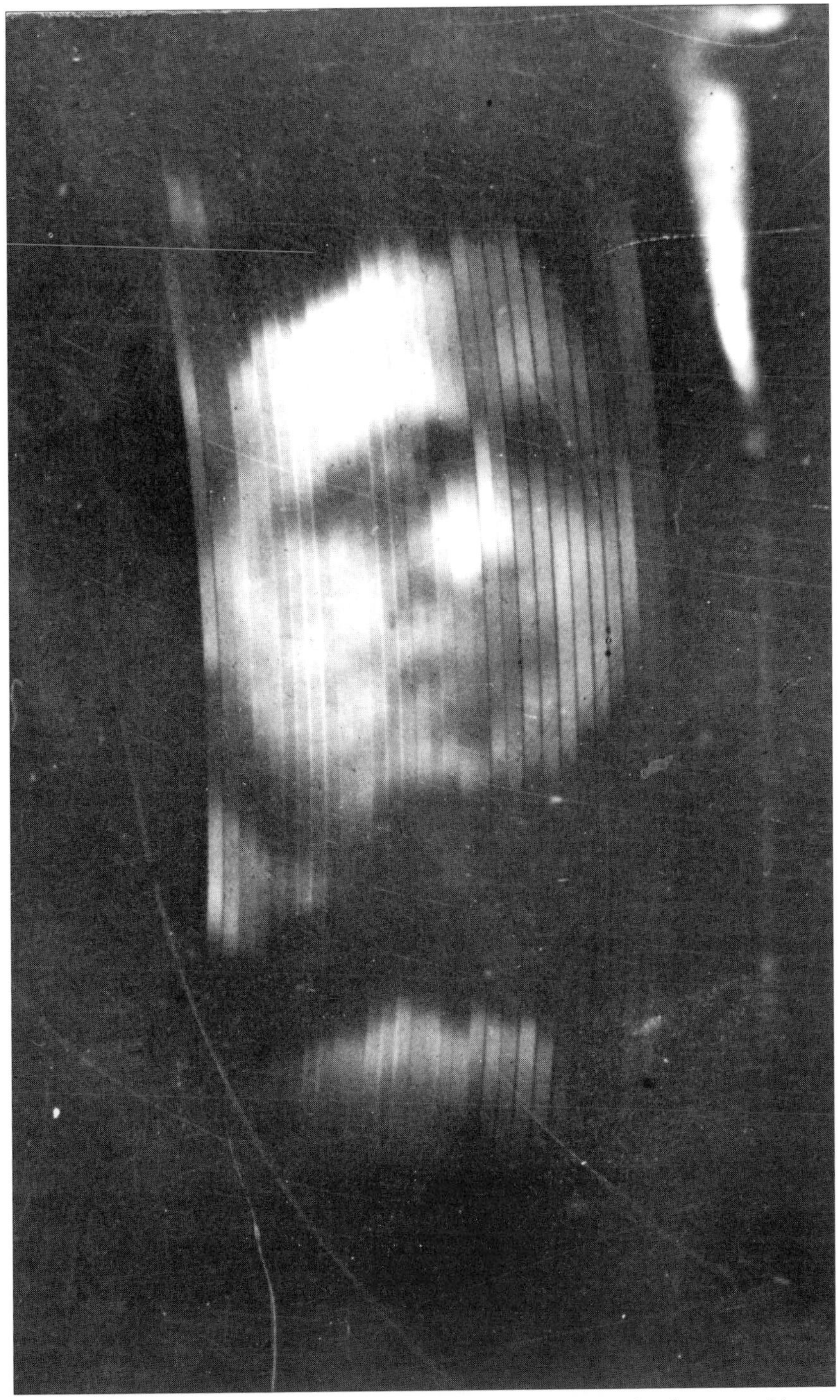

The first photograph of a television image, to which Baird refers on p.64. (National Museum of Photography, Film and Television)

space, I made endless measurements and ultimately decided on a long narrow picture in the ratio 7 high by 3 wide. The number of lines was arrived at by making drawings from photographs divided into strips. I tried experiments with different numbers of strips from 15 upwards, and came to the conclusion that 30 strips and a picture frequency of 12½ per second was the best compromise. The amount of detail which could be sent at that time was limited by the wireless transmitter. This also limited the number of pictures per second which could be sent out. It was a compromise between flicker and detail.

More flicker—more detail; less flicker—less detail. So I decided on a picture with a fair amount of flicker and a fair amount of detail. The picture I got through was surprisingly good considering the small number of lines. The photographs shown do not do the results justice. Much is lost in the photograph and much more is lost owing to the fact that photographs can only show a still picture, whereas the movements continually presented new aspects and the effect was obtained of much greater detail than the photographs can show.

I have, however, reproduced them to give an indication of the results obtained. The picture reproduced, which represents the first television image ever photographed, was taken by Lafayette. An exposure was given of 3½ minutes. I wanted it taken by an outside photographer to prove that it had not been faked or retouched. The sitter was Hutchinson who had his head fastened in a vice arrangement to enable him to keep still for 3½ minutes.

In testing out the amplifiers I used to use headphones and listened to the noise of the vision signal made. I became very expert in this and could even tell roughly what was being televised by the sound it made. I knew, for example, whether it was the dummy's head or a human face. I could tell when the person moved, I could distinguish a hand from a pair of scissors or a matchbox, and even when two or three people had different appearances I could even tell one from the other by the sound of their faces. I got a gramophone record made of these sounds and found that by playing this with an electrical pick-up, and feeding the signal back to a television receiver I could reproduce the original scene.

A number of such records were made (and one can be seen at the Science Museum in South Kensington) but the quality was so poor that there seemed no hope of ever competing with the cinematograph.[4] If the cinema had never been invented the 'Phonovisor', as I christened the device, might have been

4 Recently, Donald F. McLean has used computer enhancement to play back some of the original phonovisor recordings. Details are given in his book which is listed under Further Reading.

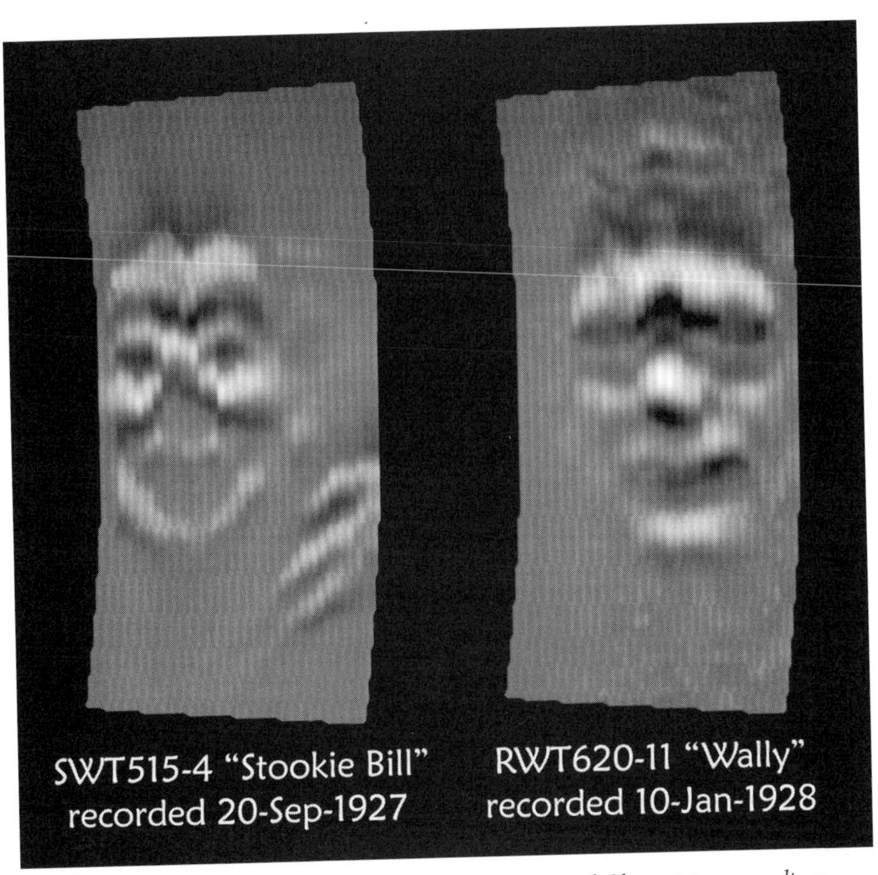

Digitally restored single images from the experimental Phonovision recordings; quality is not as good as that of 30-line images of the day. On the left is one of the Stookie Bill dummy heads mounted on a tripod; the operator's hand can be seen bottom right. This is the earliest-known video recording, believed to have been broadcast during the transatlantic transmission tests of November 1927. The image on the right is of Wally Ffowlkes, a popular human subject for Baird's television experiments. (Donald McLean)

worth developing; it was certainly an intriguing process. Vision into sound and sound back again into vision.

One of the visitors to my laboratory in 1926 was Professor Andrade[5] who wrote in the *Encyclopaedia Britannica* describing it. One of his remarks was, 'What I like about your work is that you make no effort to get publicity'. This intrigued me considerably, as I was doing everything in my power to attract public attention to my work, knowing that it was my only hope of raising money. He had mistaken inefficiency for modesty.

5 Prof. E.N. da C. Andrade (1887-1971) was a popular science writer and held the chair of physics at University College, London, for many years.

Professor Andrade wrote a very fair account of what he saw for the *Encyclopedia Britannica*. It appeared in the next issue. In the following issues, unfortunately for me, the articles were written by Dr. Ives, a rival employed by the American Telegraph and Telephone Company who gave very full prominence to the work of the his company and completely ignored the fact that I had demonstrated television more than a year before his company. The *Encyclopedia Britannica* is owned by a U.S.A. concern and has to cater for a U.S.A. public.

One of the visitors to our laboratory in 1926 was Mr. Leo Amery, at that time Colonial Secretary. He arrived accompanied by a small army of officials, who came up in the lift to our laboratory in St. Martin's Lane (it was on the fourth floor) but Amery himself ran up the four flights of stairs to the amazement of Sir Edward Manville[6] and myself who were waiting to receive him. He explained that he never went in lifts, but if possible always ran upstairs to keep himself fit as his hobby was mountaineering.

I think our demonstration was rather a disappointment to some of the officials. We were showing in a disused cinema exhibition room and they expected, I think, to see our television picture thrown on to the cinema screen, and found that they had to look into a peep hole and see a little picture a few inches square. Amery himself, however, had more vision and realized the potentialities of what he was seeing. He is one of the many men who combine small stature with the highest mental attainment and physical efficiency. I have often thought that men 6ft.6in. and broad in proportion are much more cumbersome and much more expensive in upkeep than men 4ft.6in. and narrow in proportion who need less food and take up much less room in buses, and that we should breed small men.

The idea occurred to me in 1926 that it should be possible to use infra-red or ultra violet rays in place of light, and so be able to send an image in complete darkness. I tried ultra violet rays first; at this time my only assistant was the office boy[7] imported from Hutchinson's soap works, who was ignorant but amiable. The ultra violet rays affected his eyes, and he did not complain, but I got a fright and tried infra-red. I first used electric fires to get these infra-red rays which are practically heat rays. I could not get any result and added more fires until Wally was nearly roasted alive; then I put in a dummy's head and added more fires. The dummy's head went up in flames. I decided to try another track and use the shorter infra-red waves. To get

6 Sir Edward Manville became chairman of Television Ltd. when the company went public in 1927, see Chapter Six.

7 This was 'Wally' Ffowlkes, who was later to be a subject of Baird's experimental phonovision recordings (see photograph p.65).

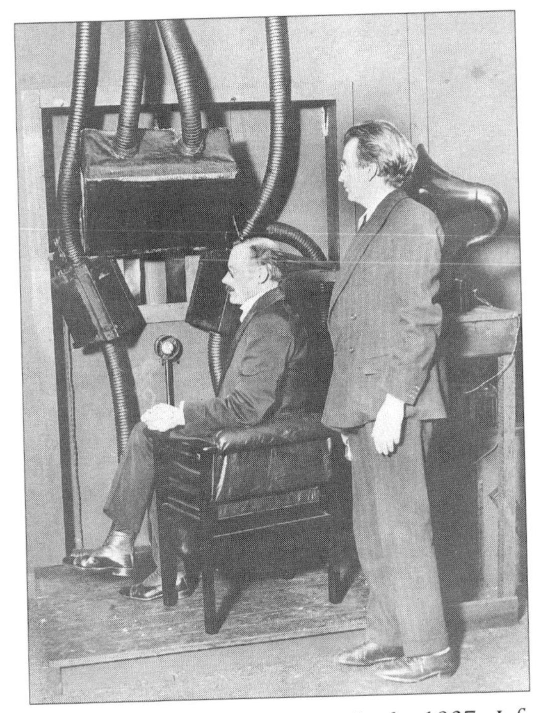

Noctovision at the British Association meeting in Leeds, 1927. Infra-red radiation is given off by the hot ebonite plates. The sitter is Dr Clarence Tierney, whose head is clamped in position. The flexible tubes carry air, an essential requirement for removing excess heat.

these I used ordinary electric bulbs covered with thin ebonite. This cut off all light but allowed the infra-red ray to pass. Wally sat under this without much discomfort and after one or two adjustments I saw him on the screen although he was in total darkness. That was again a thrill, something new and strange; I was actually seeing a person without light.

Hutchinson was shown the wondrous phenomenon and great excitement prevailed. Again the members of the Royal Institution were called in to witness the new phenomenon and again the scientists and newspapers were summoned. Sir Oliver Lodge[8] came with his daughter and said it was amazing but very hot, and did not sit long, which I thought was a pity, as he was the best subject for television I have ever seen. His white beard and impressive head came through marvellously well.

The newspapers gave this invention, which I called 'seeing in the dark', great publicity which had one rather amusing result. At that time I was staying in a small residential hotel and one morning when I came down to breakfast

8 Sir Oliver Lodge (1851–1940) was one of the pioneers of radio. In his later life he became interested in spiritualism.

a young lady resident asked me 'Is it true, Mr. Baird, that you have an apparatus which can see through brick walls and in the dark?'

I said 'Yes' and she said 'That explains the queer tickling sensation I had last night'. That is, of course, a quite exaggerated and wrong view to have of the powers of television as it is today but some time in the future it may be possible to do what the young lady dreaded, although if this does happen it will be a very doubtful blessing for everyone concerned.

It was not long before another very peculiar application was suggested.[9] One day a bent up elderly man appeared in the board room. He was a professor and a distinguished entomologist and he had a very strange story to tell. It appeared he had been called in to investigate the activities of a medium called 'Marjorie', which was the name the medium was known by, although more strictly speaking it was the name assumed by her controlling spirit. The earthly 'Marjorie' was a respectable married lady who in early life had lost her only son in tragic circumstances. This boy 'Jack' one morning in a fit of depression had gone into the bathroom and cut his throat, leaving the razor with bloodstained thumb marks on the floor; this razor had been locked away untouched. 'Marjorie' was heartbroken and in an effort to speak again to her son joined a spiritualistic circle. Here she was discovered to have astounding mediumistic powers.

In the darkened silenced room of the spiritualistic circle she sank into a trance; in this state her body exuded from its orifices a strange vapour called ectoplasm. This extraordinary substance floated about her like a cloud and was of such a fine and mysterious nature that it could be used by the spirits to build ectoplasmic bodies. It was now that the spirit of Jack her departed son appeared and made his presence felt. Not only did he speak and answer questions, but he used the ectoplasm to materialize his hand and shook hands with the audience, wrote messages and moved objects and did all that a hand floating in space could do. It was at this stage of the proceedings that the professor was called in as an independent scientific observer to test and report on these astounding phenomena.

He approached the whole matter with complete scepticism, and went to work with the careful thoroughness of a highly trained scientific observer. He was however badly handicapped as all manifestations had to take place in a completely dark room, ectoplasm being highly sensitive to light which instantly destroys it, with dreadful results to the medium, profuse bleeding and even death—such was the tale. Nevertheless, the professor persevered, the

9 The next few pages relate to Baird's interest in spiritualism. A few years ago these episodes formed the basis of a Scottish film project entitled 'The Visual Purple', but it did not get beyond the script development stage.

mystic hand materialized and the professor shook hands with this ectoplasmic manifestation. The hand, he said, felt hard and cold like the skin of a serpent, but of its existence there was no doubt.

Then he was struck with a really brilliant idea, no two thumb prints were alike, why not get Jack's ectoplasmic hand to make a finger print and compare it with the prints on the carefully preserved razor. This extraordinary experiment was carried out, Jack was readily persuaded to press his ectoplasmic hand on a piece of carefully prepared wax. The prints so produced were compared with those on the razor; they were identical. The professor had heard that I had a device which enabled a person to see in the dark. He wanted to borrow this so that he could watch the whole process of materialisation without destroying the ectoplasm.

I agreed at once to take part in this and he went off to arrange matters. I never saw him again, he was killed in a motor accident. A spiritualist told me that this was undoubtedly the action of the spirit forces and the result of his effort to pry into sacred secrets.

This was not, however, the end of the matter. Sometime afterwards a caller arrived at the company's office with an invention for me to examine. It was a little electric motor controlled by a tuning fork. He had it with him but had some difficulty in making it run properly. I suggested he should come back when the troubles were overcome. He rose to go and as a parting shot said: 'Would you care to have definite and irrefutable evidence of the survival of the personality after death?' I said, 'Yes, I would give everything I possessed for such evidence'. 'Well' he said, 'I can give it to you if you do not mind making a journey'. I said 'I would go to the ends of the earth for such a cause.' 'There is no need for that' said he, 'you have only to go to West Wimbledon'.

This was arranged and I duly arrived at the address given, a small highly respectable villa where I was welcomed by a party of elderly ladies and gentlemen and given tea. Then the medium arrived, a neurotic nervous looking woman of about 35. We trooped up to the seance room. Here there was arranged a circle of chairs and in the centre of this a small box like a sentry box, draped in black, provided with a chair. The medium was handcuffed to this chair. The audience sat round on the other chairs provided, each person held a hand of each of his neighbours and put a foot on one of his neighbour's feet, so that any undetected movement of hand or foot was impossible. Lights were then extinguished. The leader, an impressive elderly gentleman with side whiskers, then led the singing of a hymn, 'Tis a beauteous belief that spirits round us throng'. This was followed by a prayer. Then darkness and silence, broken only by a mysterious steady humming sound, which I learned afterwards came from an electrical tuning fork, the rhythmic sound being found to assist manifestations (also possibly to mask any noise made by the medium).

We waited and waited, the darkness and silence had a most eerie effect, then the old lady next to me squeezed my hand and whispered in an awe-struck whisper, 'look, it's coming'. Sure enough in front of the booth, faint and almost invisible, a wavering purple coloured cloud was forming. It grew denser and then the silence was broken by the irregular tapping of a morse key. The spirit was signalling by tapping in the morse code. The message was directed to me and it came from no less a personage than Thomas Alva Edison.[10] Edison had, it appeared, been experimenting with noctovision in his home in the astral plane; he was convinced that it would in time prove of great use in assisting communication between the living and those who had passed over, but the time was not ripe, and to attempt to use it now would incur grave danger. He was however continuing his research and would communicate with me when the time came to use noctovision. Here his message stopped and Edison left and gave place to another control called Lilly.

Lilly was more domestic in her messages and gave detailed advice to one of the circle upon what to do for her rheumatism and how to handle various family troubles. I remembered that I had a lunch appointment and time was passing, and so I whispered to the leader that I had an engagement and if he would excuse me I would slip out. A horrified whisper replied to me, 'if you move you may be struck dead'.

I murmured that under the circumstances I would wait. However the spirits took the hint and a few minutes afterwards heavy groans came from the medium. She was coming out of the trance, the lights were turned up, the leader hurried into the box with a large glass full of something hot and steaming, and soon the medium was sitting up looking about her in a dazed way. I slipped out, bade a hurried and apologetic good-bye and arrived at my luncheon nearly an hour late.

My guests, two hearties from Scotland, were still waiting; drinking beer over lunch I told them where I had been and what I had seen. 'It seems all tosh to me', said one. 'I wonder how sensible people can waste time with that nonsense', said the other. 'Well', I said, 'What about Sir Oliver Lodge, Conan Doyle and other men of similar standing, you can't brush them aside with vulgar noises'. 'Oh,' said the first, 'they are people who are perfectly sane except on one point. I once knew a man who was not only sane, but

10 Thomas Edison died in October 1931, which places this episode at a later date, therefore out of sequence with this part of the memoirs.

extremely clever, but he was under the delusion that one of his legs was made of glass'.

'It's not that' said the second, 'old Lodge and these other old boys wanted to get into the limelight, the press won't give any prominence to their ordinary activities, but they get a good show for spooks, the public will always read about that sort of thing. Of course it's all a lot of damned rot'.

I might have agreed with them, but I have witnessed some very startling phenomena under circumstances which make trickery out of the question—and also unfortunately, publication. I am convinced that discoveries of far-reaching importance remain waiting along these shadowy and discredited paths.

The spiritualistic seance endeavours as its object to prove the survival of personality after death. I had an intriguing experience not connected with the survival of personality but connected with the problem of what this personality is.

An exceptional mechanic could make a very good imitation man. Memory would be supplied by a library of talking picture films. The creature could easily be made to react to light and to the spoken word, so that it would guide itself, its movements being actuated by some kind of television device which would make it able to move without striking the furniture. It would be able to answer questions, the sound of the voice operating a device which would return on a gramophone arrangement giving the proper answer. Real man might be considered as some sort of very perfect mechanism of this type, plus something else. This something else is usually designated as the personality and, by the old-fashioned, as the soul.

I had a very startling experience of seeing a body with the soul absent. When I was an engineer I shared a room with another man; one night when I was just going to sleep he woke me up by asking me if I knew anything about the Sea of Azov. I said I fancied that it was very shallow.

'Ah yes,' he said, 'but is it wet?' 'Of course it's wet'. 'Oh well,' said he, 'we must use armoured cable'. I realised he was dreaming and I found that so long as I answered him in accordance with his dream we could hold lengthy conversations. That night in the dream in which I co-operated we called in Stibbs and his gang of navvies and solemnly laid a cable across the Sea of Azov. Night after night, I took part in these extraordinary conversations. In the morning he remembered absolutely nothing of what had taken place. His sleep personality was utterly distinct from his waking personality. Sometimes in the middle of this dream state he would come awake with a sudden exclamation, 'What was that, did you speak?' He had no recollection whatever of what he had said a moment before. While he was in the sleep state it was possible to conduct him from one scene to another by easy stages by making suggestions to him. He had no will whatever of his own.

Unfortunately for the experiment he got mixed up with a young lady and this ultimately brought the whole thing to an abrupt end; but before it did so it provided one very interesting incident. They had a quarrel and he wrote a letter, in great trepidation and mental anguish, breaking off their engagement. That night in his sleep he began talking about this. 'I do not think I should have written that letter', he said. I answered in the proper spirit and suggested he should write again to her. To my amazement, there and then in the middle of the night, in almost pitch darkness he proceeded to write a letter, and put it in an envelope. He put this in a drawer and returned to bed. Next morning he remembered nothing whatever of this. That evening the young lady arrived at our digs and the quarrel was made up. They married shortly after and my investigations came to an end.

Here, however, was a case where something left the body and it became merely a bundle of memories and reflex actions, until this something came back and took control. I suppose a physiologist would say it was merely a question of the state of the blood pressure. But the fact remains that in his sleeping state he acted merely as a complicated machine over which I had complete control, then when he became awake something entered the machine and took the controls away from me. This something else would defy the skill of any mechanic to duplicate.

With television accomplished in the laboratory I was anxious to transmit over a distance and got in touch with Mr. Kirke, the Chief Research Engineer of the B.B.C. He was very interested and helpful and several transmissions were arranged, the television picture being sent from my laboratory to the B.B.C. by telephone line. Mr. Kirke then put it on the ether through the B.B.C. wireless transmitter. I received it again by wireless at my laboratory.

The pictures came through the B.B.C. practically unaltered and it is interesting to record that the B.B.C. actually transmitted television in 1926, although unofficially I was bound to silence and did not mention the matter at the time. It amused me to hear people say that while I could send television in the laboratory it could not be sent over the B.B.C. Unfortunately the transmission came to an abrupt end. Someone 'up above' at the B.B.C., Kirke would not say who, had ordered the transmission to cease.

When the B.B.C. issued this edict we applied to the Post Office for a licence to transmit television and obtained the first television licence ever issued, 2 T.V. We erected our own transmitting station with our aerial on the roof of Motograph House (now Film City House) and commenced our own transmissions to an experimental receiving station at 'Green Gables', a villa in

Harrow. With television a demonstrable fact and with the great publicity and interest aroused, the whole aspect was changed. Hutchinson, my old friend of the soap days, had reappeared and he and a friend of his, Captain Brodrib, had bought out Will Day (giving him a substantial profit).

We had no difficulty in finding fresh capital. Larger premises were taken in St. Martin's Lane and it became obvious that the next step should be the formation of a public company.

Chapter Six

After our demonstration to the Royal Institution we decided to form a public company. Neither Hutchinson nor I knew the first thing about public companies, but, after running up and down many blind alleys, we got in touch with a firm of stockbrokers, Messrs. Vowlers. They were interested and preliminary arrangements were arrived at to form a company with a capital of £120,000 if underwriters could be found.

I wrote to my cousins and again their interest and support proved a vital turning point in the enterprise. By return of post they agreed to take up £5,000. This started the ball rolling and the whole sum required was soon forthcoming. We had however a narrow escape.

In 1927 we had a complete monopoly of television. We shouted it loud and we shouted it long and it was our main prop and argument with the somewhat nervous underwriters. Ian Anderson and Risdale were our supporters in the firm of Vowlers. The other partners looked askance at the project. 'You, Ian,' said old Vowler 'have the excuse of youth for embarking on this wild adventure, but as for Risdale, his grey hairs should have brought him more sense'. However, in February 1927 the underwriting formalities were completed and the underwriting cheques handed to Charles Baker in the office of Kenneth Brown, Baker and Baker. Hutchinson and I returned to the Engineers Club to celebrate.

By an astounding coincidence, the very next morning the newspapers were filled with headlines 'Television Demonstrated in New York'—'American Telegraph and Telephone Company gives Television Demonstration'; this was happening at the very moment when the hesitant underwriters were signing the underwriting form. The A.T. & T. were breaking our monopoly and taking from us our best talking point.

The underwriters were furious. They thought it was a put-up job and wanted to back out of their contract. We pointed out that we were absolutely unaware of the pending demonstration and that we had already had fourteen months run with complete monopoly and could not expect to continue for ever to be the only people to show television. All that had happened, we pointed out, was that the A.T. & T. had made an elaborate copy of what we had been doing. They were indeed, as Dr. Dauvillier said later, 'Using Baird's methods without saying so'.

They came round and agreed to carry on, but they were considerably shaken. I was shaken myself. I had begun to regard television as something which belonged exclusively to me and our monopoly as something inherent in the nature of things, and so the A.T. & T. show was a blow, although I knew that a thing of this sort was inevitable sooner or later. Our demonstration and the whole system with drawings and details of our apparatus had been given the widest publicity. Every big electrical concern had been aroused and their experts put to work. It was surprising that we had had so long a run as fourteen months.

Our first chairman was Sir Edward Manville, a city magnate, the chairman of the Daimler and several other big companies, who was introduced by Sir James Percy, an old friend of Hutchinson. Sir James was a tower of strength, good sense and good spirits. He died soon after the company was formed, and had he lived our whole history would have been a brighter and happier one. Mr. Shortis, a vice-president of the Guaranty Trust of New York, Hutchinson and myself completed the board. Hutchinson and I were joint managing directors at equal salaries and with similar contracts, 5 years at £1,500 per annum. The formalities were duly completed and we solemnly attended our first board meeting. Sir Edward Manville sat at the head of the board and I, humbly but firmly as becoming the founder and Managing Director, facing him at the other end of the table. For 15 years I sat there. I saw first Sir Edward boom at me across the table, a florid sunset seen through a cloud of cigar smoke. He faded and for a time was replaced by the bearded dignity of Lord Ampthill, finally to be replaced by Sir Harry Greer—setting sun and cigar smoke once again.

What abject nonsense was talked around that table! Sometimes in the early days I raised a feeble squeak of protest, but an angry booming and clouds of cigar smoke from the chair soon put me in my place.

The meetings had the solemn dignity of a religious observance. The chairman commenced the service by asking the secretary to read the minutes of the last meeting, and when this long rigmarole had been read through, after a brief but solemn pause, he put the question to the meeting, 'Gentlemen, is it your pleasure that I sign these minutes?' All hands were raised in assent. Tommy Bartlett, the secretary, then read the first item on the agenda. He was well primed beforehand with what course we wished the chairman to pursue, and, being a past master at guiding chairmen, usually got the meeting through with decisions more or less in line with what Hutchinson and I had previously agreed upon.

I was busy with my wheels and pulleys and soon I came to regard board meetings as analogous to going to church, functions to be slept through. Sometimes I woke up with a start at some of the antics at these meetings and thought 'God help the shareholders of public companies'. However, after a few squeaks, I relapsed again into dreams of further permutations and combinations of wire and mirror drums and lamps.

When the company was first formed I was the only person who could produce a picture. The technical staff consisted of half a dozen or so new men who had not attained a mastery over the many weird contrivances which I then used. There were no television engineers in those days and to the wireless experts much of my apparatus contained features completely strange. The directors were much worried over this. 'Suppose something happened to Baird, the whole thing would collapse as there is no one to take his place'. So it was decided to insure me for £150,000. I was extremely unwilling and nervous about this, I remembered my card, 'Unfit for any service'. Suppose the insurance turned me down—the Directors might refuse to carry on. However, the chairman insisted, he was very good at insisting; 'I am adamant on this point' was his pet phrase.

Two doctors prodded me about, they whispered together, did more prodding and listening, whispered again, obviously they did not like the proposition, also obviously they were reluctant to turn down a magnificent bit of business, £150,000 policies are not dropped without very excellent and unanswerable reasons. Finally the insurance company decided to take the risk for twelve months at a whacking premium, £2,000 I think it was, and the situation was saved. At that time I think it was the largest life insurance policy ever taken out. Since then it has been dwarfed into complete insignificance by the Hollywood stars, but it remains a record for inventors.

To revive enthusiasm after the damping effect of the A.T. & T's demonstrations, I decided to transmit from London to Glasgow. Fortunately the telephone lines between London and Glasgow are extremely good ones, and the transmission was a great success.

Professor Taylor Jones, of Glasgow University, saw and spoke with me, as did various other civic dignitaries.

The transmission was from our laboratory in Long Acre to the Central Hotel in Glasgow.[1] It was given great prominence in the press and created a considerable sensation. Shortly afterwards I was invited to give a public address in the St. Andrews Hall in Glasgow.

This is the largest hall in Glasgow and corresponds to the Albert Hall. The

1 The transmission took place in May 1927 and was actually from Motograph House. In 1988 a commemorative plaque was unveiled by Ben Clapp and me in the lobby of the Central Hotel.

Ben Clapp (adjusting the controls) and James Denton in Glasgow, receiving television from London, May 1927. The apparatus is set up on a washstand in a bedroom at the Central Hotel. (Daily Mail)

lecture was a very grand affair with the Duke of Montrose in the chair and the Lord Provost and 'the nobility and gentry' on the platform. It was a most outstanding event for me, the return of the native. The genius from the kailyard returns to lecture to the civic dignitaries.

I arrived accompanied by Mr. Denton.[2] I had some simple apparatus to demonstrate light sensitive cells and other similar phenomena, a collection of lantern slides and a completely unsuitable lecture, far too technical. It was, I learned later, absolutely incomprehensible gibberish to the bulk of the audience, but at the time I was happily unaware of this.

On the platform sat Papa and my sister,[3] the Inglis cousins and a few friends with the Lord Provost, and other worthies. The Duke of Montrose introduced me and did it wholeheartedly. He was a great amateur wireless enthusiast and had followed the development of television.

2 James Denton was a part-time college lecturer, radio experimenter and scientific writer. He became the honorary secretary of the Television Society when it was founded in 1927. Denton was associated with Baird's work in an unofficial capacity until his death in 1945.

3 Baird's mother had died in 1924. The Rev. John Baird, now aged 85, was being looked after by his eldest daughter, Annie.

'Scotland' he began, 'has introduced many great pioneers. We have given the world James Watt, the inventor of the steam engine, Henry Bell the pioneer of the steamboat, and tonight we have with us John Logie Baird from the same town as Henry Bell, and the inventor of the great marvel of the age —television. Mr. Baird was the first man to see by television. This marvellous feat is what he is going to tell us about', and more to the same effect.

It was immensely gratifying; even Papa was impressed. I then got up and told the audience all about selenium, photo electricity, scanning and synchronism, illustrated by lantern slides, with abstruse diagrams. They were dazed but dauntlessly enthusiastic.

'My Lord Chairman, Ladies and Gentlemen, it is a great pleasure, privilege and honour to be with you tonight and I must begin by thanking our Chairman for his flattering remarks. I hope to be able to explain to you tonight something of the history and development of television. The story of television may be said to begin with the discovery of the light sensitive properties of selenium. One day in 1878 an obscure telegraph operator, a Mr. May, observed that his instruments behaved in an erratic fashion when the sunshine fell upon the selenium residue which formed part of his apparatus. This phenomenon was investigated...' and so on...

The lecture finished, a vote of thanks was proposed by the Lord Provost and received with prolonged applause. Friends and admirers and press representatives thronged on to the platform, and the occasion came to an end in a blaze of glory. It was an episode which would have delighted the heart of Samuel Smiles.[4]

I was now a celebrity, but instead of using this to get into the right circle, I turned down all sorts of invitations and continued to shuffle around in the lab in a state of dirt and dishevelment, absorbed in my bits and pieces. I paid for my carelessness later on, when big business got hold of television and of myself. Oh! Why did I not cash in while the going was good?

A laboratory with all the apparatus I wanted was to me a perfect paradise. I was thoroughly absorbed and happy, and there is no happiness to compare with the happiness of an inventor surrounded by his wires and mechanisms, trying this and trying that and ever anticipating some astounding result.

There was, however, one unwelcome intruder into my paradise. Sir Edward Manville was an engineer and felt it his duty to see what I was doing and so, ever and again, I was interrupted by the intrusion of his portly figure. He boomed at me, through a cloud of cigar smoke, innumerable pointless questions, and, what was worse, he made impossible suggestions, and when I tried

4 Samuel Smiles wrote a best-selling book *Self Help* (1859), which extolled the Victorian virtues of hard work, thrift and self-improvement.

to explain that they were impossible his booming became angry and ominous, and he glared indignantly and overbearingly at me over his impressive facade of double chins.

I determined to end it all when we moved into 133 Long Acre.[5] I made the door of the laboratory just wide enough to let myself through (I was very thin in those days) and far too narrow to admit Sir Edward. The first time he appeared there was a most heart-rending and embarrassing scene—he was an obstinate and determined man—he got through! But he lost several buttons from his waistcoat and dropped his cigar and tramped on it in the process. He never visited my laboratory again.

I had been accustomed for many years to living on a very frugal diet; breakfast, bread and tea; lunch, milk with a dash, a scone and two pats of butter, and in the evening, dinner, sausages and currant bread and tea, and some days no sausages. Now with money no object and the Ivy, London's most luxurious restaurant, opposite our office door, I tasted for the first time the joys of luxurious living. Fine wines were introduced to a virgin palate, and the superb dishes of rich and strange foods for which the Ivy is noted, to a stomach trained on sausage and mashed. I plunged headlong into and wallowed in the joys of good living, all unaware of the terrible dangers that lurk in the apparently harmless pleasures of eating and drinking.

Hutchey and I lunched together; it was the high spot of the day. Commencing with cocktails we went through hors d'oeuvres, rich pea soup, fritto misto, curried chicken and Bombe Gladys Cooper, washed down with copious draughts of Chateau Y'quem, followed by coffee and petits-fours washed down with Bisque d'Bouche brandy.[6] Gorged and bloated and belching, we tottered over to Motograph House and awaited afternoon tea. Those were the days!

But they were too good to last. The cold weather arrived and I caught my usual winter chill, but this time it was complicated by liver and other disorders. I did not throw it off properly. Alarming symptoms developed, my nose swelled to twice its normal size and became a vivid crimson, and I suffered from acute catarrh. I consulted a specialist and was warned to avoid in future all wine and rich food. The Ivy days were over. Boiled fish, soda water and toast gradually restored my nose to something like its original dimension and hue, but the catarrh remained and became slowly and steadily worse—a heavy dry inflammation and sometimes pain. I went to a specialist in Great

5 The move from Motograph House to Long Acre took place in January 1928.*

6 Fritto misto is a dish of Italian-style fried food and Chateau Y'quem is an expensive, sweet dessert wine. This menu would have an effect on a normally healthy person, so its effect on Baird is hardly surprising.

Portland Street; he looked up my nose and down my throat. 'Ah, yes' he said, 'you have a polypus at the back of the nose, a small operation will remove it; it will mean a week in my nursing home, then you will be quite alright again'. I have a great dread of operations and I had hoped for something to rub in or be taken three times a day after meals.

I told him I was very busy and could not take even a week away from business at the moment, but would let him know when things slackened off. I paid three guineas and went at once to another specialist. He was a cheerful soul—I told him of the polypus, 'I see no polypus here', he said, 'but there is inflammation and discharge from the tonsils. This is poisoning your system and giving rise to the toxic condition which is troubling you. You had better have them removed, a quite trivial operation'. I paid him three guineas and tried again (three guineas meant nothing to me at that time). I kept my mouth shut with the next man, he said it was inflammation of the antrum. The antrum should be washed out. 'Quite a small and painless operation'.

I tried again and got another antrum diagnosis. I tried again—'Ah, this comes from your teeth. Your mouth is a positive graveyard, the gums must be cleared before we can even get to the root of your troubles'. I tried again, this time it was sinus trouble. I had my head and teeth X-rayed, I called on my own dentist. He said, 'It's a ramp, your teeth have nothing to do with it'.

I tried again and this time the man was too quick for me—he had an electric iron up my nose and burnt out some imaginary growth before I realised what he was doing. My nose was in a bad state for days and since then has been much worse. Over a period of years I tried again and again, I made almost a hobby of it. 'Clear the gums' and 'Wash out the antrum' were the favourites, running about 50/50.

My last effort, however, had an element of tragedy. I was told of a wonderful new treatment by injections. Off I went, sceptical but not without hope. I had a swab made of the discharge and this was found to be full of streptococci. These germs were in the blood stream and the cause of the trouble. The remedy was simple, a growth was cultivated from the streptococci out of my nose, this colony was then killed and quantities of their dead bodies were injected into my blood stream three times a week (at 10/- a time) for six months. These dead germs stimulated the phagocytes so that on this diet they became more numerous and virile and destroyed the live streptococci, the cause of the trouble. I was reminded of Shaw's 'Doctors Dilemma' but there was no operation and no nursing home, and money in those days was plentiful. The surgeon had a convincing and pleasant manner. Three times a week I solemnly went to the surgery and had something injected in my arm—it made my arm a little stiff but otherwise did no harm. I had been

Colour television in 1928. This sketch was made 21 years later, based on a contemporary photograph. Major Church is at the right of the picture.

having the treatment for about six weeks when it had to be discontinued as the surgeon's own catarrh trouble had developed into mastoid and he was in his own nursing home. Since then I have left doctors alone, my catarrh gets steadily worse and occupies a prominent place among the various ills which affect my ageing body; it struggles for precedence with my congested liver and weak lungs.

I was intensely interested in the possibilities of colour television, and early in 1927 began experimenting. I used a disc with three spirals of holes, one covered with a red colour filter, one with blue and one with green. Light passed through these spirals successively, so that red, green and blue pictures were sent out. They were received and recombined on a similar disc at the receiver. The results were quite striking and very fascinating, although the pictures were only an inch or so square. We found that strawberries came out particularly well and they were popular with the staff.

This device was demonstrated at the British Association meeting in Glasgow in 1928. This was the first time that colour television was shown in public.

Following the colour experiments I experimented with the possibility of transmitting a complete illusion of reality, that is an image both in colour and

Baird in the late 1920s with Sydney Moseley, 'a stout and jovial man, with a merry and wicked twinkle in his eye...'

in stereoscopic relief, and my next step was to make an apparatus transmitting stereoscopic images. This was comparatively simply done by using discs with two concentric spirals, one spiral dealing with the image seen by the left hand eye and the other dealing with the image seen by the right hand eye. The images at the receiver were blended by viewing through a stereoscope; with this device quite effective stereoscopic relief was obtained and I gave several demonstrations. I intended to combine this with colour by using two sets of three colour spirals, but never carried out the experiment.

Shortly after the company was formed, I came into the board room and found Hutchinson in earnest conversation with two men who were considering investing in the company. One of these, a stout and jovial man, with a merry and wicked twinkle in his eye, immediately attracted me. It was Sydney A. Moseley[7] who was to play a very prominent part in our future activities. Both Hutchinson's and my knowledge of high finance was infantile and this was also true of our knowledge of journalism. We were both much upset because a little wireless paper, quite unknown to the general public,

7 Sydney Alexander Moseley (1888–1961) was a successful journalist and writer who had served as a war correspondent in World War I. He had a mischievous sense of humour and an outspoken manner which appealed to Baird but which were disliked by stiffer personalities such as Lord Ampthill and Sir John Reith. Reith in his diary referred to him as 'the miserable Moseley'.*

had seen fit to make capital out of us by publishing criticisms, just bordering on libel and utterly unfair and prejudiced.

We talked to Moseley about this and he said he would fix it, and he did. The next issue of our persecutor[8] contained an article by Moseley refuting all the previous attacks and hailing the invention as a great achievement. From that day on his position was established. He became one of the family and I welcomed him with open arms. What a relief to have a man about the house who took a real interest in our affairs.

Those directors who sit on dozens of boards were of no use to me. I'm sure that often they sat at the board of the Baird Company without being quite certain what we dealt in, whether it was glass bottles or artificial silk. But it did not matter. So long as they said at intervals in loud pompous tones, 'I agree with the chairman', and did not fall asleep, they were all right. I remember on one occasion one of them did fall asleep and caused the chairman some embarrassment by snoring audibly. He was quietly and discreetly awakened by the secretary.

Moseley was not the sort who fell asleep at board meetings or anywhere else where money was involved.

We had removed our aerials from Motograph House and erected a couple of impressive masts on the roof of 133 Long Acre, and had also equipped a small studio from which we sent out regular transmissions of television. It was, however, our wish that the B.B.C. should broadcast for us and in an effort to get the decision which had put a stop to Mr. Kirke's activities reversed, I wrote to Sir John Reith and he replied cordially and invited me to visit him.

Arriving at the B.B.C. I was ushered into a little waiting room. After a few minutes the door opened and Sir John entered. Twenty years had elapsed since I had seen him, a young student of the Royal Technical College. The youthful heavy lad had fulfilled the promise of his youth. It was an imposing presence which stood in the doorway; the large gaunt frame was surmounted by a grim rugged visage, surmounted in turn by a domed forehead, rendered more impressive by a heavy scar. Sir John was affable and cordial and we talked for nearly an hour, he seated at his desk beneath his stained glass window, in his vast office at Portland Place.[9]

He was at that time, I think, really wishful to be friendly; he offered to support a government grant to my company for the furtherance of our research. We parted in a very friendly fashion, but it was not to continue.

8 The 'little wireless paper' was *Popular Wireless* and Moseley's article appeared on 22 September 1928.*

9 The B.B.C. did not move to Portland Place until 1932. In the late 1920s they occupied more modest premises at Savoy Hill.

Sir John Reith and his wife Muriel, whose uncle was W.J.B. Odhams, the publisher who had helped Baird in Hastings, see Chapter 4. (B.B.C.)

Our relations with the B.B.C. formed such a tangle of intrigue and conspiracy and cross purposes, that which threads of the web were involved at any one time is, I now find, extremely difficult to remember. What with Hutchinson weaving one web to suit his particular purpose, Moseley weaving another to suit his ends, and various other gentlemen at the B.B.C. weaving their own little personal webs for no very particular purpose, what was actually going on was not very clear to me even at the time.

Our cordial relations with Sir John culminated in a little private party in the Pinafore Room at the Savoy. The only members of this little party were Reith, myself and, of course, Sydney Moseley. It is a strange fact but I cannot remember one single thing which was discussed at that lunch, but we were all very frank and parted on the best of terms. It was the last time I ever conversed with Reith.[10]

In 1927 we gave a show of Noctovision to the British Association meeting at Leeds.[11] Mr. Denton and I proceeded to Leeds and with the aid of the local

10 There were in fact a few later meetings between Baird and Reith. On 2 January 1931 Reith wrote in his diary that he had 'found him [Baird] most reasonable'.*

11 The British Association meeting at Leeds took place in September 1927. The year has been corrected from 1928 which was given in Baird's typescript. The B.A. meeting of 1928 was at Glasgow.

carpenters erected in a hall in the Municipal Buildings a complete transmitting and receiving equipment. It was an extremely successful show. Successive parties were formed in the transmitting room which was in total darkness, and placed one by one in front of the transmitter in the dark room. They were seen on the screen in an adjoining room, a queue being formed which passed before the screen. The spectators were apt to linger and Hutchinson, who was acting as M.C., made himself extremely unpopular by hustling many eminent dignitaries of the scientific world who were not accustomed to such treatment. 'Pass along, please. Pass along. Now then, sir, now then, you can't stand there all day—others wish to see as well as you'. The papers boomed the show and such a crowd gathered outside the Municipal Buildings that mounted police had to be called to control the crowd—a thing unheard of at a B.A. meeting.

It was all, however, perhaps not quite at the level of dignity deemed desirable by certain of the scientists and did not do me much good in some academic circles. Professor Howe of Glasgow University, although a gentleman with a usually acid pen, gave the show a good puff in the *Wireless World*—'A credit to all concerned'. Denton and I felt duly gratified as we had worked all night for two nights running before the demonstration opened.

It was at this B.A. meeting that the Television Society[12] was formed. Denton and I had many times discussed such a society and we thought 'now was the time'. Mr. W.G. Mitchell[13] had been attracted by our show and had been very helpful to us, standing at the door and controlling the queue and mitigating some of Hutchinson's exuberances.

We held a little meeting and Dr. Tierney, myself and Denton gave speeches, following which founder members were enrolled. Denton and Mitchell wanted me to be President, but I thought it better if some completely independent man of high standing in public life could be found. On the other hand I wanted to be associated with the Society, so, to have me in the Society and to put me on a proper pedestal, I was elected the sole and only Honorary Fellow and the articles of incorporation provided that there should be only one Honorary Fellow—myself.

Shortly after this, W.C. Keay arranged for me to be present as a guest of honour at the annual dinner of the Caledonian Club. The other guests of honour were the Prime Minister, Mr. Ramsay MacDonald, and Lord Haldane of Cloan.[14]

12 The Television Society received its Royal title in 1966.

13 Mitchell became hon. secretary (lectures) while Denton was hon. secretary (membership).*

14 Lord Haldane (1856–1928) had had a long political career with the Liberal party and his main achievement was the reform of the reserve system of the British army in the years prior to World War I.

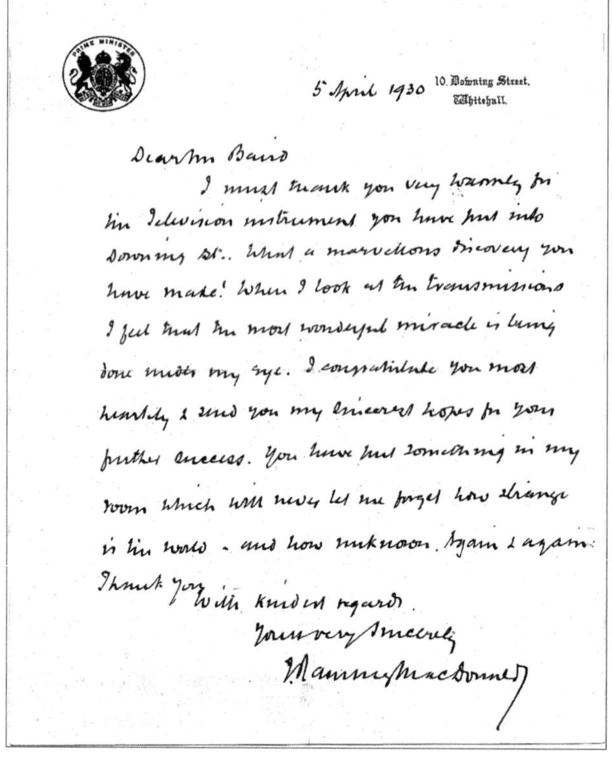

PRIME MINISTER

5 April 1930 — 10, Downing Street, Whitehall.

Dear Mr Baird

I must thank you very warmly for the Television instrument you have put into Downing St.. What a marvellous discovery you have made! When I look at the transmissions I feel that the most wonderful miracle is being done under my eye. I congratulate you most heartily & send you my sincerest hopes for your further success. You have put something in my room which will never let me forget how strange is this world – and how unknown. Again & again thank you.

With kindest regards.

Yours very sincerely

J. Ramsay MacDonald

'[Ramsay MacDonald] sent me a very nice letter...' (Royal Television Society)

Lord Haldane was very interested in television and later when approached by Mr. Keay agreed to become the first President of the Society.

The Prime Minister was also greatly interested. He and Lord Parmoor[15] visited Long Acre and saw each other by television. Then we showed them noctovision. The Prime Minister was at first sceptical and could not credit that the man he watched was in absolute darkness, so Lord Parmoor went into the darkroom. 'I see you again,' said Mr. MacDonald, 'are you really in the dark?' 'Absolutely black!' said Lord Parmoor, over the phone, 'I am moving my hand in front of my face and I can't see it'. 'I can', said MacDonald and needed no further proof. Later on he had a television set installed in 10, Downing Street and sent me a very nice letter about it.

I became a member of the Caledonian Club early in 1928 through Lord Angus Kennedy who was one of its staunchest supporters and oldest members. This led to my giving a private demonstration to Edward, then Prince of Wales. We installed a receiver at the Club and arranged a special television

15 Lord Parmoor was Lord President of the Council in MacDonald's Labour government of 1929–1931.

programme to be sent over the line from our studio in Long Acre. I dined together with the other members of the Club at a dinner given to the Prince of Wales. After dinner, in the usual sweat of apprehension, I went up to the reception room. The image was coming through well. The Prince of Wales was ushered in by Lord Inverforth[16] complete with double chins, bay window, pompous affability and a large cigar.

The Prince of Wales shook hands affably, a smallish, thin, youngish man. He looked at the little flickering image and recognized Miss Farrar[17] who had a large cows-lick wisp of hair which helped recognition. 'Very interesting—Amazing—Did you invent this?—Remarkable—Still a good deal to be done before it rivals the cinema. How is it done?—Must have taken you a long time'. Such was the nature of his remarks to which I replied in a fever of embarrassment and apprehension for fear that the apparatus, which was developing precarious symptoms, would break down.

The gathering, after twenty minutes, departed in an atmosphere of cigars, white waistcoated corporations and a faint aura of old brandy. The cordial boomings and throaty laughter faded down the corridor. 'Damn good thing they have gone', muttered the engineer who was looking after the apparatus, 'the bloody motor's nearly red hot'.

16 Lord Inverforth (1865–1955) was chairman of the Marconi Company and was later to become Chairman of Marconi-EMI which competed with Baird Television. See Chapter 9.

17 Gwen Farrar was a well-known singer who often performed with Jack Hylton's band.

Chapter Seven

Early in 1927 two men visited our little laboratory in Motograph House, an elderly American gentleman with a pretty young wife, and a stout and amiable young gentleman from London. The latter was a Mr. Clapp;[1] the elderly American was a representative of the Woolworth Company.[2] Their suggestion was that we should transmit television from London to the Woolworth Company in New York. Mr. Clapp was an amateur wireless fan who had an experimental wireless transmitter and had suggested to Woolworth that they should approach us. Nothing came of it at the time, but Clapp himself was an attractive fellow and shortly afterward when he gave up his wireless business, I engaged him as my second assistant. I had by that time two other assistants, Mr. Denton, whom I had met at Hastings, always obliging and appreciative, and the invaluable Wally.

The company expanded rapidly and we took large premises at 133 Long Acre, more assistants were engaged, we bought up Clapp's transmitting apparatus in Purley and decided to have a shot at transmitting across the Atlantic. There was absolutely no technical reason that I could see against it.

Wireless speech on short waves was being regularly sent from London to the USA by numerous amateurs with quite insignificant apparatus and if speech could go so could television. But it took in practice a good deal of doing. Clapp and Hutchinson went over to New York to arrange for reception and I started to transmit, sending the television signals by telephone line to Purley where they were put on the ether by a transmitter operating on a wavelength of 49 metres.

Mr. Denton and I spent night after night at Motograph House, listening to the whirr of the transmitter and hoping for the best. The only time at which the transatlantic transmission could be made was from about midnight onwards, and I had on one occasion to explain to a suspicious policeman our mysterious activities in the small hours of the morning.

1 Ben Clapp actually joined Television Limited in November 1926. He lived until 1990 and in his later life he was of immense help to television historians. In 1987 he was presented to H.M. The Queen at a reception to mark the diamond jubilee of the Royal Television Society.

2 The company was Wanamaker's, not Woolworth.

James Denton at the controls of the television transmission from London to New York. (Royal Television Society)

All sorts of troubles arose; Clapp cabled that the tuning fork we used for synchronizing the generated waves killed his reception. I cabled back telling him to put it in another house and connect it by telephone. That cured that trouble, then our signals were too faint and with great difficulty we increased the power of our transmitter.

In the midst of this we had to move our plant from Motograph House to Long Acre. There we had more success and Clapp reported having seen faintly the image of the dummy's head on his screen; more success followed and we decided to give a press show. All was arranged and Elissa Landi[3] was to be the first face sent across the Atlantic. She arrived with her agent and we waited to hear from New York that our signals were coming through. We waited and waited, but something had gone wrong. Elissa Landi and I spent the night together; I did what I could to console her with sandwiches and champagne, but it was to her a disappointing night. However, it enabled me to tell my friends that I had spent the night with Elissa Landi and create a momentary sensation, until the circumstances were explained.

The next night we tried again; this time the lady chosen was the wife of a

3 Elissa Landi was an Italian-born actress who appeared in many films of the 1930s including *The Count of Monte Cristo* (1934) in which she co-starred with Robert Donat.

On 9 February 1928 Mrs Mia Howe was the first lady to be televised from London to New York. (Royal Television Society)

Television reception on board the Berengaria *in mid-Atlantic. Hutchinson is at the extreme left of the picture. On his left is Stanley Brown, the radio officer whose fiancée's picture was transmitted from London. (Royal Television Society)*

journalist.[4] I did not dare to ask any more 'stars' but journalists are accustomed to the frailties of machines and human beings and sympathetic to disappointments. This time, however, there was no disappointment. Mr. Clapp telephoned from New York that it was coming through well. The dummy head was moved away and when Mrs. Howe took its place, the message came through that they could see a lady's face. The press on the other side had witnessed the reception and the story came back red hot from New York. 'Atlantic spanned by Vision', 'Television conquers the Atlantic'. These and suchlike headings blazed across the evening and daily papers.

On the voyage back from New York we staged a further demonstration, sending television from 133 Long Acre to the *Berengaria* in mid-Atlantic. The picture came through well and created quite a sensation on the ship. Then I had a stroke of luck. I was able to get hold of the chief wireless operator's fiancée and get her to come in front of the transmitter. The wireless operator[5] did not know she was to be there, but recognized her immediately she appeared on the screen.

The shares in the company rushed upwards. Fortunes were made by active speculators while I sat like my own dummy and neither bought nor sold, and did not make one penny. I see some supercilious physicist asking what useful purpose was served by this transmission. Just so, that is what the expert navigators of Spain said when Christopher Columbus sailed across the Atlantic. What good purpose did arise out of this and similar efforts? A very big purpose was served; research all over the world was stimulated and investigators in every country had it forced down their throats.

Television was proved a practical possibility. These transmissions and demonstrations broke fresh ground and stimulated progress in an incalculable degree. I was not interested either in shares or money or stimulating progress but I felt I was doing something worthwhile. It was interesting enough to make me willingly work night after night until three and four in the morning. These were happy days; I lived in the laboratory surrounded by my apparatus, trying this and trying that. Ominous clouds were gathering on the horizon and threatening rumbles were becoming audible, but they were still far off.

The trouble started with an estrangement between Hutchinson and myself. First of all he took to sitting at the head of the board room table and using the board room as his office, relegating me to a little back room. I resented being made to look like his subordinate while he, I think, resented my monopolizing the limelight. Jealousy was at the root of our trouble; it came to a head when the name of the new public company came to be

4 Mia Howe was the wife of the Associated Press representative in London.

5 The wireless operator was Stanley Brown and his fiancée was Dora Selvey.

settled. I wanted it called Baird Television Ltd., and he wanted it called British Television Ltd. He said the name Baird limited the scope of the company; it should be all embracing. He had the prospectus printed with the name British Television Ltd. I lost my temper and told him he could form his own company and call it what he damned well liked and I would form my company and call it Baird Television. That was the last I heard of British Television, but our relations were hopelessly strained. The company was split into two camps, a house divided against itself. Into this unpleasant and intriguing atmosphere entered the cute and crafty Sydney. For a little while he was not sure on which side to throw his weight. I think at first he inclined to Hutchinson, but after a brief and uneasy period of having a foot in both camps, he came over definitely to allegiance with the Baird faction. We had much in common; to me he came as a gift from heaven although many thought otherwise and saw in him nothing but an arch villain and tried to make out that he was crafty, unscrupulous, seeking only his own interest, ready to twist and turn and betray and ruin us all if it would benefit his pocket.

My position was a most difficult one. I had no business friends; plenty of acquaintances, plenty of contacts, yes, but no friend; no one who spoke my language, no one with whom I would willingly have spent a minute more than was necessary for the purpose in hand. I was uneasy and bored in the company of my colleagues and they in mine. But it was not so with Moseley, firstly I think because he had an outstandingly shrewd and acute mind and a keen sense of humour; secondly he was utterly devoid of false dignity and pompousness, and free of the hypocrisy and humbug which are their accompaniments. I had served an apprenticeship as a fitter among the lowest of the working class, hard brutal men in hard brutal surroundings driven from morning to night by the fear of poverty and destitution never far behind.[6] In these surroundings dignity and decorum had short shrift and even now, in moments of acute stress, I am liable to break into a flood of Saltmarket eloquence, sufficient in its foul brutality and obscene imagery to cause a Billingsgate porter to cover his ears in horror.

The transatlantic transmission had resulted in enormous publicity and interest, both in Europe and the U.S.A. and we were advised that an immense opening existed in America. We decided to form an American company and indeed in the first flash of success we decided to form companies in every country of the world. Hutchinson was overflowing with enthusiasm and we hoped to establish a world position in television. In this atmosphere Ian Anderson was again approached and his firm arranged the underwriting of a

6 See Chapter 2 and the episode with 'Big Gibson'.

£500,000 company, Baird International Television Ltd. This company bought from Baird Television Development Company Ltd. all foreign rights in the Baird inventions. Hutchinson and myself were joint managing directors at £3,000 per annum, each. Baird Television Ltd. also continued functioning, and we continued to receive from this company £1,500 each as managing directors. Lord Ampthill of Ampthill[7] was appointed Chairman of the new company. Mr. Shortis, a Vice-President of Guaranty Trust Company of New York, Colonel Winch of Winch the brewing concern, Hutchinson and myself, completed the Board.

In Germany, intense interest was created by our demonstrations. Dr. Bredow, the managing director of the German Broadcasting Corporation, came over to England accompanied by his two chief technical experts, Dr. Bannertz and Dr. Reisser. He subsequently invited us to send representatives over to Germany and install a transmitter in the Berlin Broadcasting station.

I found myself arriving at the Adlon Hotel in Berlin complete with Hutchinson, a great load of apparatus and a team of technicians, and last, but dominating the whole picture, Sydney A. Moseley. Hutchinson had done the preparatory work and done it well. Our apparatus was erected at the German Broadcasting House, the Reichrundbrienk, and a meeting was arranged, presided over by the State Secretary of Posts, Telegraphs and Telephones, Dr. Bredow, with the Reich Postmaster Dr. Crowirow, chief engineer Dr. Bannertz and all those interested in television. Finally a Company was formed to develop television in Germany under the auspices of the German Post Office. The Baird Company were to supply the television, the Zeiss Company were to supply the parts relating to vision, the Loewe Radio Company were to supply the wireless parts and the Bosch Company were to supply the electric motors then used. Dr. Bannertz, the chief technician of the German Post Office, was appointed consultant. This Company was duly incorporated, the four concerns having equal shares, and so Fernseh A.G. Ltd. came into being. For some years we kept a number of engineers permanently in Berlin and I spent much time there and happy visits they were until Hitler stepped in.

While we were very successful in Germany, we made little progress in France. We had a steady stream of visitors to Long Acre and many representatives of French interests, but the results were far from satisfactory. I remember most vividly two outstanding figures, Messieurs Barthelmy and Le Duc who represented a very big French firm, the Compteur de Gaz. We gave them demonstrations, we dined and wined together, there were visits to

7 The 2nd Lord Ampthill (1869–1935) was an able administrator. Soon after graduating from Oxford he became a founding member of the International Olympic Committee and then served with distinction in India; in 1904 he was acting viceroy and governor-general.*

France and they seemed as enthusiastic and full of determination to fix up an arrangement with us as we were with them. Hutchinson had a scheme to install transmitters in each of the French stations and in Belgium and Luxembourg. I actually built six complete television transmitters for this purpose. We had interminable meetings with solicitors and long incomprehensible agreements were drawn out in English and French, but something went wrong and there were disagreements over this clause and that clause and it all ended in smoke. Some time later Barthelmey started up his own system of television, using no doubt what he had seen in London. I don't blame him; I think we had every opportunity to conclude an agreement with the Compteur de Gaz, but this was messed up.

After this we were approached by two young Frenchmen, Messieurs Leon and Stoyanowsky.[8] They were full of zeal and with them we actually got a French company going. Our engineers went over to Paris and one of the activities of the French Company was the erection of a television telephone between Paris and Lyons. Messieurs Leon and Stoyanowsky, however, had difficulty in raising capital and they introduced the Pathé Nathan Company, a large cinema concern. Monsieur Nathan himself came over to London, saw a demonstration and was favourably impressed. An agreement was concluded, but Pathé Nathan was itself in financial difficulties. After interminable running backwards and forwards to Paris, the whole of our French activities ceased with nothing actually accomplished.

In the meantime regular transmission of television had been going on nightly from our Long Acre studios. Our programmes were published in the press and we were making and selling receivers. A large number of amateurs also constructed their own, so that in effect we had a separate broadcasting system independent of the B.B.C.

We sent out quite elaborate programmes from Long Acre and even sent out a little play, 'Box and Cox', and our transmissions were not only seen by the relatively small television audience, but were heard by the general public, if they tuned into our wavelength, as many of them did.

One morning a rather unpleasant incident took place. Our engineers were fooling about in the studio singing vulgar songs and making rude remarks in front of the microphone. Unfortunately, by some accident the wireless transmitter had been left on and this vulgar programme was broadcast to the public. Next day the newspapers were full of headlines, 'Mysterious vulgar broadcast', 'Mystery station interrupts B.B.C.', and so on. Fortunately, although we were naturally suspect, it was never traced to us.

8 Anatole Stoyanowsky was a Russian national. In 1936, in conjunction with Baird Television Ltd., he patented a system for the guidance of aircraft by infra-red rays.

We might have developed completely independently of the B.B.C.; we had already broken their monopoly. Unfortunately our station at Long Acre was close to the Admiralty at Whitehall, and complaints were received. Finally we were told we must close down. This put us in a quandary and we tried to find a solution of the difficulty.

Firstly we made arrangements to transfer our transmitter to Hendon, out of reach of the Admiralty. Secondly we again approached the B.B.C., who not only refused our request but attacked us in every possible way. We hit back by appealing to the Post Office. We gave demonstrations to their chief engineer, Colonel Sir John Lee and his then assistant, Colonel Angwin; they reported favourably to the Government and considered that the B.B.C. should give us facilities for broadcasting. The B.B.C. then had a demonstration. Admiral Carpendale, the Controller, P.P. Eckersley, the chief engineer and numerous other officials arrived. They turned the whole thing down. We again approached the P.M.G. and finally a committee of members of Parliament was formed under the chairmanship of Lord Clarendon to investigate the situation. The B.B.C. was represented by Sir John Reith and Admiral Carpendale, advised by Captain Eckersley and his assistant Mr. Ashbridge (now Sir Noel Ashbridge, chief engineer of the B.B.C.).

I was to set up a transmitting station at the B.B.C. headquarters at Savoy Hill and transmit a television programme through 2LO; this programme was to be witnessed on 8 receivers of the type to be sold to the public. Four of these receivers were to be situated at the G.P.O. at St. Martins Le Grand and viewed there by the Post Office experts and certain members of the committee, four other receivers were to be placed at the B.B.C. headquarters at Savoy Hill and viewed by the B.B.C. experts and the other members of the committee. It was a nerve racking ordeal; we were to stand or fall by the result of one crucial demonstration; a wire slipping or a valve burning out at the critical moment, and the demonstration would be a failure and we would have been faced with a devastating fiasco. I spent a dreadful night on the top floor of Savoy Hill where we set up our transmitter and everything seemed to be well by the morning. I then set out for St. Martins Le Grand accompanied by Sir Ambrose Fleming.

Here in a large hall on the first floor the four receivers were installed, and soon to my infinite relief they were running properly and we were receiving images of the artists we had assembled at Savoy Hill. Mr. F.R. Phillips, who was in charge of the P.O. arrangements, notified the committee who trooped in headed by the impressive figure of Lord Clarendon. They took their places in front of the receivers and watched the little show. We had prepared for them a simple enough programme; it consisted of the head and shoulders view of singers and comedians, but an unexpected turn was however provided by Captain Eckersley, who himself went before the transmitter and was seen by the committee. The show was a complete success, but I knew that several persons on the committee were far from well disposed and awaited the report with some apprehension. Soon after, we received the report which was also published in the press. It was favourable beyond what I had hoped; the demonstration was, in their words, 'a notable scientific achievement' and they recommended that we should be granted facilities to transmit television by the B.B.C.

This demonstration was a turning point; it gave a crushing answer to innuendos and implication, hints and significant shruggings of shoulders, implying that the whole thing was a fraud or a trick. A government committee, with the greatest experts in the country, had put the invention through a rigid and drastic test and as a result had reported that they found it to be 'a notable scientific achievement.'

The B.B.C. bowed to the decision with a very bad grace and did what they could to give us as small facilities as possible and make conditions as difficult as possible. Hutchinson and I attended a conference at Savoy Hill with Admiral Carpendale in the chair, and were offered a quarter of an hour, once a week after midnight; we were to pay all expenses including all the B.B.C's. We were naturally indignant and long arguments and more and more conferences took place. Time was passing and at last rather than be held up indefinitely, we agreed—as a preliminary—to having three half hours a week from 12 midnight. On September 30th, 1929 the first transmission took place and the proceedings were opened by Sir Ambrose Fleming followed by Professor Andrade, Major Church and a short programme of artists. Sydney Moseley acted as announcer. These television transmissions were to last for a period of six years until September 1935 when the service was stopped to give place to the ultra short wave transmissions. While the ultra short waves which are now used have a limited range, the old transmissions went through the ordinary B.B.C. channels and could be received all over the country.

The transmissions took place from 11 to 11.30 p.m. with a further two transmissions a week from midnight to 12:30. The Baird company not only had to pay the expenses of these transmissions, but in addition had to pay the B.B.C. for the use of their radio transmitter. On the 22nd August, 1932 after we had made considerable agitation over the expenses we were incurring, the B.B.C. agreed to take over the programmes, and thus in some measure relieve us of the financial drain of maintaining a large programme department and paying for the artists together with the studio expenses. The arrangements were, however, still very unsatisfactory from our point of view. The

The first issue of Television, *March 1928. (Royal Television Society)*

B.B.C. took over our apparatus and two of our engineers (Mr. Campbell and Mr. Bridgewater[9]) but did not pay us one penny, using our apparatus completely free of any charge. We were indeed behaving more like a philanthropic institution for the benefit of the television-minded public, than a business concern, for there was a very big television public, even in those early days. This was proved not so much by the number of television sets we sold, although we had sold nearly 1,000 of these, as by the immense number of amateurs who built their own sets which in those days were comparatively simple and well within the range of home constructors. The immense public interest is, moreover, proved by the fact that when we started a magazine *Television*, 150,000 copies of the first issue were sold. Our apparatus was returned by the B.B.C. when the transmissions stopped in 1935, and is now in the Science Museum at South Kensington.[10]

9 Thornton H. Bridgewater (1908–1997), known to his friends as 'Tony', rose to become Chief Television Engineer at the B.B.C. from 1962 until his retirement in 1968. In 1992 he wrote a monograph for the British Vintage Wireless Society entitled *Just a Few Lines* about his experiences with the 30-line system.

10 The apparatus is now at the National Museum of Photography, Film and Television in Bradford.

The days when we had our own transmissions and our own studios provided plenty of excitement and plenty of colour. Our little studio was frequently thronged with artists; we paid them £1.1.0 to £2.2.0, but many of our best turns were unpaid, the novelty and excitement were sufficient inducement. Our studio manager was Mr. Bradley, a brother-in-law by marriage of Sydney Moseley, who had a wide experience of the stage, and ran the studio on professional lines. I remember how strange it was to come down from the cold austere laboratory to the exotic atmosphere of the studio, mysterious with young females floating about in tights, red nosed comedians applying grease paint, and colourful figures in wigs and lurid costumes. Pianists and violinists would be rehearsing with all the general colourful chaos of back stage. Then having seen the transmission through at one in the morning, I would take a taxi from the stand at Long Acre and drive the 25 miles to my lone villa on the top of Box Hill, where Winkle[11] and Mephy sat before the great log fire.

The journey cost 30/- but in those days money was a secondary consideration. On the top of Box Hill the road was very bad and on a foggy night the journey could provide adventure. On one occasion I fell asleep, and the driver missed the road and took me nearly to Brighton before I woke up. On another occasion the taxi ran off the road and charged down the side of Box Hill, finishing up with a crash of glass and a flood of blasphemy from the drunken driver in a clump of bushes. The Swiss Cottage was a most beautiful and romantic spot; it had at one time been a shooting box of the Duke of Marlborough, whose country seat was at Deepdene, a few miles away: a great mansion set among the trees above Dorking and clearly visible from my front windows. Mephy stayed with me at Box Hill and acted as a kind of general manager, supervising the two maids and the gardener-chauffeur. When I was at home we spent happy hours tramping over Box Hill, recalling the past. When we climbed the bridle path leading up the chalky side of the hill, Mephy strode in front, a gaunt figure in a flapping black highland cape, his long grey hair floating in the wind and grasping in his hand a great forked staff. One day we passed a lady with a little girl and I heard her whisper loudly, 'No dear, that's not Jesus'.

Captain P.P. Eckersley was the chief engineer in the B.B.C. at the time of the beginning of our transmissions. I had never met him and he had been hostile and had written articles casting doubts on television, with implications that there was something fishy about the whole business. Our demonstration through 2LO, however, convinced him; in fact he actually took part in the programme given to the parliamentary committee, appearing on the screen

11 Winkle was a cat.

The Swiss Cottage on Box Hill, Baird's home from 1929 to early 1932, '...a most beautiful and romantic spot'. (Ray Herbert)

and saying a few words. When we began our transmissions I had a very hectic dinner with him and Noel Ashbridge at the Savoy. Eckersley I found a most entertaining and human personality and I got on extremely well with him. This was before the days of my total abstinence and we entertained ourselves lavishly. At about eleven Ashbridge had to go and catch a train, but Eckersley and I remained over our old brandy until after one in the morning, and parted the best of friends. 'If we had only met sooner', said Eckersley, 'all this trouble over television would have never arisen'.[12]

For years the studio remained at Long Acre but when in 1932 the B.B.C. took over completely, our apparatus with Mr.Campbell and Mr. Bridgewater our two operating engineers went to the B.B.C. headquarters where the first B.B.C. television studio was erected. The programmes were directed by Mr. Robb and a very good job he made of them. Mr. Birkinshaw was appointed chief television engineer.

Shortly after our studio had been moved to Broadcasting House, a very spectacular and ambitious demonstration was given by us in cooperation with the B.B.C. A Danish newspaper *Politiken*, which was much interested in television, arranged with us to install a large screen in Copenhagen and give

12 Soon after this meeting, Eckersley (1892–1963) was forced to resign from the B.B.C. because he had an affair with the estranged wife of a colleague and, worse still, had let this be known. He was succeeded as Chief Engineer by Ashbridge.*

demonstrations in their Arena Theatre. These were given at first from a local transmitter in Copenhagen. Towards the end of the demonstrations, however, on November 8th 1932, the normal television broadcasts from the B.B.C. in London were picked up in Copenhagen some six or seven hundred miles away, and thrown on the screen of the Arena Theatre. The transmission was part of the regular nightly television transmission sent out by the B.B.C. but a special programme was arranged for the occasion, including Carl Brisson the famous Danish actor. Curiously enough the Arena was the theatre in which he made his debut. The reception was extremely successful and aroused an unexpected amount of interest.

We sent expeditions all over the world, fulfilling our claim to be international. One expedition went to Australia and gave numerous demonstrations in Sydney.[13] Another expedition under Lord Angus Kennedy went to South Africa and gave demonstrations at the British Association meeting there, and Hutchinson himself went over to the U.S.A. filled with the hope of forming a vast American company. He might have done, I think, had he not been ambitious. Week after week and then month after month went by and nothing definite matured. When at last he did return with a heavy bill for expenses and no definite deal accomplished, he found a very impatient board awaiting him. Some exceedingly unpleasant meetings followed, culminating in Hutchinson resigning from the board. He did receive, however, an 18 months option on the American rights and was thus given an opportunity to make good the American deal which was, he believed, in the offing. He returned to the U.S.A. armed with his option, but the golden moment had evidently been lost and when the 18 months elapsed nothing had resulted.

In the meantime Sir Edward Manville had resigned, Sir James Percy had died and with Hutchinson's resignation the board consisted of Lord Ampthill as chairman, myself as managing director, Colonel Winch and Mr. Shortis.

13 The Australian demonstrations were set up in Melbourne in December 1928. The South African demonstrations were given at Cape Town and Johannesburg.*

Chapter Eight

With Hutchinson's resignation the company was without a business manager and Mr. Napier, a friend of Colonel Winch, was appointed to this job. His appointment was a mistake; he actually retained his position as manager of another company and tried to do the work on a part time basis, dividing his activities between the two companies, a hopeless arrangement. Baird Television needed, and badly needed, a whole time business manager. The only real driving force on the business side was Sydney Moseley. Our relations with the B.B.C. were in his hands. He was a close friend of Gladstone Murray,[1] at that time regarded as Reith's understudy. Sydney was a realist and recognised that the business was being conducted on far too expensive a scale. He urged me to make drastic cuts and here I ran across the path of Napier who, with his staff, formed a very expensive item. We had a succession of unpleasant meetings but at last the obvious fact that our cash was becoming dangerously low forced the board to action and Napier went. I then succeeded in getting Moseley on to the board and a wholesale cutting down of expenditure followed. I even agreed to reducing my own salary by half.

In the meantime technical progress continued. The first patent I ever took out described a television screen consisting of thousands of little lamps, something after the style of the electric publicity signs in Trafalgar Square where the lamps light up to form figures and letters.

In 1929 I made one of these with considerable difficulty. It consisted of 2100 little flash-lamp bulbs forming a screen about 6ft x 3ft. It gave a remarkably bright and spectacular television picture. It was very coarse owing to the relatively small number of squares of light and shade out of which the picture was made up, but the effect was brilliant and striking. We erected it on the roof at Long Acre and demonstrated it to the booking agent of the Coliseum. He was enthusiastic and shortly afterwards we were topping the bills at the Coliseum as 'Baird British Television', with three performances daily. All sorts of celebrities appeared, transmitted from our studios at Long

1 Major William Ewart Gladstone Murray was a Canadian with a distinguished service record (D.F.C., M.C., Croix de Guerre) in World War I. He had joined the B.B.C. in 1924 and held the rank of assistant controller (information). In 1936 he became general manager of the newly founded Canadian Broadcasting Corporation.*

Baird took this picture of Sydney Moseley standing by the large screen made up of 2100 small bulbs, on the roof at 133 Long Acre in the summer of 1930. (From S.A. Moseley, The Private Diaries of Sydney Moseley, *1960)*

Acre and were seen by the audience. We got a splendid reception—'startling success which convinced the most sceptical', said the Daily Mail. Many others spoke to the same effect.

Among the celebrities who were televised from Long Acre to the screen were the late Lord Baden Powell, the Rt. Hon. George Lansbury, Sir Francis Goodenough, Lt. Cmdr. Kenworthy, Lord Marley, Frederick Montague (Under Secretary of State for Air), Sir Nigel Playfair, Herbert Morrison (Minister of Transport), Miss Ishbel MacDonald, Miss Ellen Wilkinson M.P., Sir Oswald Moseley, Miss Irene Vanburgh, H.W. Austin (tennis champion), and the pugilists Young Stribling and Bombardier Billy Wells.[2]

The demonstration at the Coliseum was opened by the Lord Mayor of London, Sir William Waterhouse.[3] He appeared on the screen and, after saying a few words, his image held a conversation with his wife, who was in a box. I remember the conversation ended with Sir William saying, 'When do

2 In this list of 1929 celebrities, Lord Baden Powell is still remembered as the founder of the Boy Scouts. George Lansbury was a senior Labour politician and grandfather of the actress Angela Lansbury. Baird has misspelt the surname of Sir Oswald Mosley who was an up-and-coming Labour M.P. in 1929 but shortly afterwards became the British fascist leader. He was interned in World War II.

3 Actually Sir William Waterlow.

we dine?', and his wife replying, 'At eight o'clock'. The image from the screen then replied 'I will be there'.

So great was the public interest that the 'House Full' notice was a common sight during the three week visit of the television screen. We had an arrangement with the Coliseum to get half the takings above the normal takings of the corresponding period of the previous year. Altogether we made approximately £1500.

The screen created a great deal of interest throughout the continent and we received contracts from the Scala Theatre, Berlin, the Olympia Cinema, Paris, and the Rodeokvarn Cinema in Stockholm. The screen with a staff of operators was sent to Europe and demonstrated in each of these places with great success.

The screen was also used on the occasion of the B.B.C.'s first play by television: 'The Man with the Flower in his Mouth'.[4] This was produced by Lance Sieveking[5] and he did it with great skill and went to immense pains to make the best possible use of the limited power of our 30-line apparatus. We built a great canvas tent on the flat roof of 133, Long Acre and turned it into a small theatre where a select audience saw on a large screen the play, which was being broadcast from Savoy Hill. A fierce wind was blowing and as the tent was none too well fastened down I was in terror that the whole thing would be blown off the roof, distinguished audience and all. Part of the structure was on wheels and was altogether very rickety and an extra strong gust of wind might well have wafted it over the edge into Long Acre.

One of our visitors was Marconi. Colonel Winch, one of our directors, knew him and he had asked to see a demonstration. He was a rather pale middle aged man, with somewhat of the aloof politeness and the little bow and smile which one usually associates with royalty. He duly inspected the image and Colonel Winch was televised for his entertainment and also of course Mr. Moseley. 'Yes, very good, most interesting' said Marconi. 'Are you carrying out any research on television?' I asked. 'No', said Marconi 'We are very busy now with research on short wave transmission and overcoming the fading problem'. And so with further compliments and everyone bowing and smiling he took his departure. On going out, however, he stumbled on a loose rug but was saved from falling by the ever watchful Sydney and so, accompanied by Colonel Winch, he departed down the stone steps of 133, Long Acre. That was the first and last time I ever saw him.

4 A one-act play by Luigi Pirandello.

5 Lance Sieveking (1896–1972) was a poet and novelist as well as a producer and writer of radio drama. In 1967, he again produced 'The Man with the Flower in his Mouth' on 30 lines, but this time as a tape recording under the auspices of the Inner London Education Authority. In 1970, the 40th anniversary of the original production, it was re-enacted before B.B.C. cameras.

The first televised play in Britain, 'The Man with the Flower in his Mouth', 1930. Lance Sieveking, the producer, has his spectacles pushed up on his forehead. (Royal Television Society)

Marconi was a man for whom in some respects I had a great admiration; he played every card with such consummate skill and ability. Every advantage was grasped and consolidated. All rivals were asked into the fold or crushed. Alliances were formed with those too big to be roped in and too powerful to crush. With his powers as an inventor or a scientist, however, I was not so much impressed. Men like Dr. Fleming and De Forest have contributed far more to the art in the way of invention than Marconi. Nevertheless although the invention of no single device of fundamental importance can be attributed to Marconi, it was he who ventured forth like Christopher Columbus and forced upon the attention of the world the existence of a new means of communication. Sir Oliver Lodge and others state, and with truth, that his experiments were well known to them and other workers in physics. Hertz had shown and demonstrated wireless waves much earlier and Hughes had sent and received signals by wireless with primitive apparatus long before Marconi. But neither Hertz nor Hughes, nor yet Lodge and his co-workers, had taken these laboratory devices, pieced them together, and compelled the world to take notice that here lay a new system of communication capable of immediate practical development and of incalculable value.

He knew the immense importance of professing profound religious conviction and it is reported that he told the press how his great invention of wireless had come to him while he was on his knees in prayer. Aloof dignity he had carried to a fine art. When he tripped over the rug in our laboratory and was saved from falling headlong by the arms of Sydney Moseley, even this did not crack his dignified reserve. A man who could continue and maintain such an attitude in such a situation, borders on the superhuman.

Another celebrity I met at this time was Bernard Shaw. I was posing for a film[6] called 'Signpost to Success'. I was to represent Invention; Bernard Shaw, Drama. The film showed a cartoon of the example and this gradually faded to give place to the living face. While I waited Bernard Shaw entered, a tall gaunt old man with vital twinkling eyes. 'Ah yes,' he said 'television I know, I've seen it on at the B.B.C.' Then he was called away to get into the set. The subject of the film was phrenology and the lecturer explained where the various bumps of drama, creative art, poetry and imagination were on the craggy cartoon of Bernard Shaw. The cartoon then melted away, disclosing the face of Mr. Shaw himself. 'Don't believe a word of that nonsense' said Mr. Shaw. 'These bumps have got nothing whatever to do with it. The man with most bumps I have ever met was an imbecile coal heaver', and he went on in this style to tear up the unfortunate lecturer.

Sir Ambrose Fleming was a frequent visitor and an enthusiastic and powerful supporter. He was a really marvellous old man when I first met him. Though approaching his eighties he was as keen and alert as many a man in his twenties. His invention, the thermionic valve, revolutionized wireless communications and is in my opinion by far the most valuable invention of the 19th century. Broadcasting is entirely based and dependent upon this valve and untold millions are invested in it. Fleming however, made little out of it either in fame or fortune. He was employed by the Marconi Company as a consultant at the time of his invention, which became their property and the valve became the Marconi Valve. He was not however altogether forgotten twenty years after his invention. When one of the greatest industries in the world had grown up as the result of his pioneer effort, the British government reluctantly and at long long last conferred upon him a knighthood. Poor Fleming! If he had only been a crafty opportunist, or had had a few friends among the county gentry and done a bit of hunting and shooting, or even if he had had the intimate acquaintance of a few publicans[7] with their half-witted cronies at the Club, he would not have had so long to wait. This protracted

6 It has not been possible to trace this film.

7 Baird is probably using the word 'publicans' in its biblical sense, meaning 'tax collectors' or, more broadly, senior civil servants.

delay in recognition hurt and embittered the old man, as well it might, and is a lasting disgrace to our government.

An immensely important addition to Fleming's invention was made by the American, Lee De Forest, who added a 'grid', so making this valve an amplifier and thereby provided the missing link which the whole electrical world (including myself) had been looking for. De Forest did little better, in fact I think he did even worse than Fleming. I met him many times and liked him, a man of the world with a real sense of humour and no swollen head. Unfortunately there was no good feeling between Fleming and De Forest. The latter said Fleming's valve wasn't an invention at all; that it had been described by Edison and used by Eister & Guitel. The only invention about the valve, he said, was his insertion of the grid. This was not fair; neither Edison, nor Eister and Guitel, nor anyone else, ever thought of using the Edison effect to provide a wireless valve. Anyone could have done it, but nobody did until Fleming arrived. Anyone could have discovered America but Columbus did it. This was the view taken by the U.S. High Court in the action between the Marconi Company and De Forest.

I had a difficult few minutes once when I was giving Fleming a demonstration and De Forest arrived unexpectedly. However I managed to avoid a meeting which might have been highly embarrassing. When Lord Haldane died, Fleming became president of the Television Society and gave it his wholehearted support.

Our programmes from Long Acre became more and more ambitious and in 1931 I fulfilled a long held ambition and televised the finish of the Derby. It took months of work. We had a large van at Epsom, opposite the Grandstand, and in this a television transmitter pointed at the winning post. From here, a telephone line conveyed the television signals to 133, Long Acre, and from there they were sent over another telephone line to the B.B.C. where they were broadcast. The reception was by no means perfect but the horses could be seen and at that time it created great interest.[8]

The next year (1932) I used the same van for a still more ambitious experiment and fitted up a large screen 9 ft. x 6 ft. at the Metropole Cinema, Victoria. The transmitter was the same as that used the previous year and consisted chiefly of a large revolving mirror drum. The picture sent out by the B.B.C. was narrow and upright in shape, seven parts high to three parts

8 In the original typescript, Baird had used the phrase 'quite a sensation'. A handwritten comment appears in the margin; 'There we are again! Everything that happens "creates quite a sensation". Try and invent, as you are an inventor, some new phrase.' This tart comment may have come from Baird's journalist friend James Spence. Baird changed the phrase to 'great interest'.

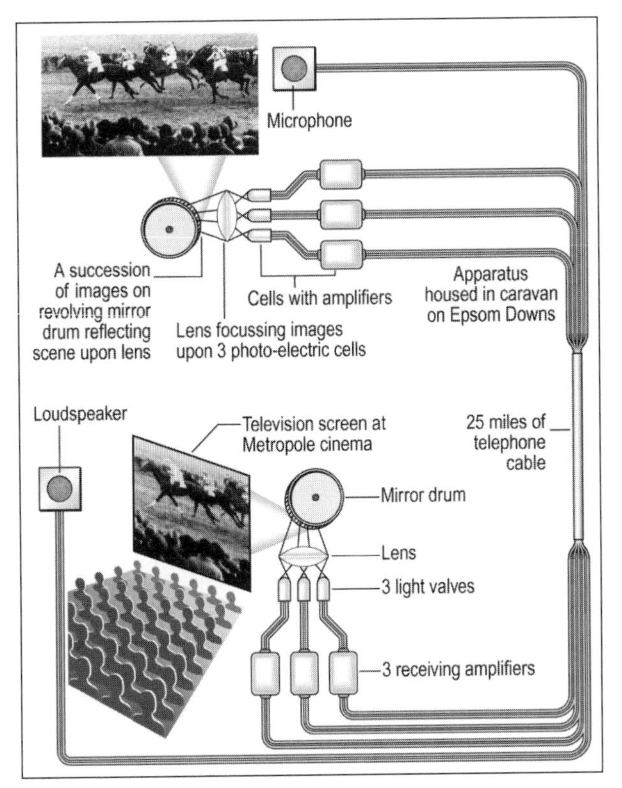

The mirror-drum system used to televise the Derby in 1932. Redrawn by Robert Britton (National Museum of Scotland).

wide. To give a large picture at the Metropole I had three pairs of telephone lines from Epsom race course and sent out three pictures side by side, these being reproduced side by side on the cinema screen to make up one wide picture nine feet wide by seven feet deep. This demonstration was one of the most nerve-racking experiences in my television work, second only in anxiety to the demonstration given to the Parliamentary committee in 1929.

We were up all the night before the show putting finishing touches to the apparatus. When the great moment drew near I remember standing beside the apparatus literally sweating with anxiety, the perspiration dropping off my nose. A vast audience had gathered in the cinema. Even the passages were packed and the entrance hall and the street outside were filled with a disappointed crowd unable to get in.

If the show had been a failure, which might easily have happened, the audience would probably have wrecked the house. I should have been a complete laughing stock. However, all went well; the horses were seen as they paraded past the grandstand before the race and when Optimist, the winner, was seen flashing past the post, the demonstration ended with thunderous

The 'Televisor' was the world's first mass produced television set. It sold for 18 guineas (£18.90).

applause. I was hustled upon the platform to say a few words but was too overcome to say more than 'thank you.'

Shortly after Moseley became a director, he and I endeavoured to strengthen our position by bringing a friend of mine, Major Church,[9] on to the Baird Television board. I first met Major Church on the occasion of the transatlantic transmissions. Mr. Keay brought him along; they had been associated upon some political committee and Major Church was interested in television. He came on several nights and was there when we gave our press demonstration. Church proved a keen supporter. He was a born fighter who had made his own way in the world and had a keen and brilliant intellect. He knew a great number of people in the scientific and political world. True, he was a Labour member of Parliament and therefore somewhat suspect among the old and crusted Tories. But had he been one of the old die-hards he would have had little time for me, or I for him.

9 Archibald George Church (1886–1954) had a science degree and had served with distinction in World War I and in the Russian campaign of 1919, winning the D.S.O. and the M.C. He was elected to parliament as a Labour M.P. in 1923 and again in 1929. While Church was on the board of Baird Television Ltd. (1931–39) he kept many letters and papers, to which Antony Kamm and I had access in writing *John Logie Baird: A Life*.*

Through Church I made contact with Bruening the German Chancellor and many other important and influential personages. As it happens I neglected these contacts, but that was my fault. I had neither the energy nor the social ability to follow them up. Dinner meetings in clubs and social gatherings of all sorts were to me a perfect nightmare of physical and mental distress. The thick smoky atmosphere, the heavy food, the drink, upset me completely. After a public dinner I was generally ill and took several days to recover. Nor did I make any effort at these functions. The noise and confused cross-currents of conversation reduced me to a numbed stupor.

Our German company had progressed from strength to strength and for a time it had practically a monopoly in Germany. Then the Telefunken Company entered the field. Telefunken is the German arm of the great Radio Corporation-Marconi group, whose tentacles cover the whole world and which endeavours either to engulf or to destroy all serious competitors. The Fernseh however, with the backing of the German Post Office, more than held its ground and in 1939 was still the leading television company in Germany. We did well out of Fernseh thanks to Major Church, without whose efforts we might well have lost everything. When Hitler came to power it was decreed that Fernseh must be wholly controlled by Germany so that it would have been comparatively easy for the other partners, the Zeiss, Bosch and Loewe companies, to have frozen us out without paying us a penny. Major Church however fixed up an arrangement whereby we retained an affiliation which gave us all rights arising from our joint development in the British Empire; and in addition we were paid in cash the full value of our shares in the company.

The periodic visits I used to make to Germany in the early days were for me a time of extraordinary happiness. The dry clean air of Berlin acted as a tonic and the comfort of the big German hotels far surpassed anything I had met with either in London or America.

Church was a close friend of Chancellor Bruening and he took me several times to meet him. A quiet studious impressive figure, I felt he was more of a scholar than a statesman. The last time I saw him was shortly after Hitler came into power when his life was in extreme danger. Church and I visited him in a villa outside Berlin where he was staying with a friend. I remember the talk ranged on the reformation of the race by sterilizing the unfit. His friend opposed it. 'It is,' he said 'too great a shock to the soul.' Bruening nodded in agreement. I was struck by the use of the word soul in a discussion of this kind until I remembered that Bruening was a devout Catholic.

When I first visited Berlin, I went at once, like most English visitors, to the Adlon, being told that it was the best hotel in Berlin. Church however dispelled this illusion and pointed out that the Adlon was built and run with the express purpose of exploiting the U.S. and English tourists and that the real leading hotel was the Kaiserhof, to which I transferred myself. There for the first time I saw Hitler, who was just beginning to be a power in Germany.

Hitler seemed to me to be a man built on exactly opposite lines to the studious Bruening. He sat near me in the lounge of the Kaiserhof where every afternoon he took tea surrounded by some dozen of his supporters; Goering and Goebbels were no doubt amongst them, but I did not recognise them; at that time, they had not blazed into prominence. Hitler, however, could not pass unnoticed; he sat at the head of the table, his eyes with a strange fixed look stared in front of him from under a shock of black hair. He sat erect and silent and unmoving except occasionally when some member of his party whispered respectfully to him, when he would bow or shake his head. The gathering regarded him as a god. I gaped fascinated at the scene. One of the hotel waiters approached and warned me discreetly to look elsewhere. Nazis in brown shirts came to Hitler's table, gave the Nazi salute, took instructions and departed briskly. It was the first time I had seen all this. I was told it was a lot of nonsense and would soon fade away. The man was simply a fanatic followed by a few out-of-works and others of no importance.

My next visit to Berlin found Nazis everywhere, Nazi officials on guard at every stall in the Radio Exhibition, swarms of them in the streets, 'Heil Hitler' resounding on every side. Hitler was no longer to be seen at the Kaiserhof: he was in the Chancellery. Bruening had fled for his life and the old regime had vanished completely. A grim reign of terror had taken its place. The yearly visit to Berlin had in the past years been a delightful period, with charming happy friendly people and hotels and smiling waiters anxious to please. All this had suddenly vanished; no smile remained. The people had become grim and hostile, not openly so, but in a way sufficiently obvious. Those who were friendly and who disliked the Nazi regime (and they were many) were terrified. The streets were filled with marching men, saluting and 'Heil Hitler'-ing—it got so much on my nerves that I took the first train I could back to London and sighed with relief as we steamed out of the Frederic Strasse Station.

The coming into power of Hitler had a further effect on our Company. The Fernseh A.G., which we originally formed in Germany and in which we held equal shares with the Bosch, Zeiss and Loewe Companies, was the leading German television company. Hitler gave orders that our interest as a British concern must cease and Fernseh become wholly German. David Loewe, the head of Loewe Radio, had also been expelled from Germany as he was a Jew; he wanted us to take over the Loewe interest in the Fernseh and gain control. Fortunately Major Church was able to visit Germany and negotiate a deal whereby we got a substantial cash payment for our share. If he had not done this and acted promptly, Hitler would as likely as not have confiscated the lot.[10]

Our French activities had faded out at a total loss, as mentioned in Chapter VII. We had given endless demonstrations including a large screen show to the public in Paris at a theatre. I was not myself present at this show which was given in the very early days; but Moseley went over and acted as announcer, appearing on the screen and speaking to the audience. He was much incensed when one of the Paris papers described his presentation as a 'Bombastic Phantom'.

Our company in New York, Baird Television Incorporated, was proving a very expensive affair. We had to pay for expensive offices and staff, and the chief result of these activities appeared to be lengthy reports holding out hopes of big deals just about to mature. The board, urged on by Sydney, decided to send me to the U.S.A. to investigate the situation.[11] And so in October 1931, I set off for America in the *Aquitania*. By a strange coincidence I had assisted at the building of this ship as an apprentice in Glasgow twenty years before and it was queer to travel on it as a passenger.[12] Among the passengers was H.G. Wells and I was quite excited at the prospect of meeting a man who in my youth I had regarded as a demigod. The invaluable Mr. Knight who travelled as my secretary soon arranged a meeting and Mr. Wells, piloted by Mr. Knight, advanced along the deck to meet me. Mr. Wells proved to be a substantially built man of medium height with a cap pulled over his eyes, utterly void of any affectation or any effort to impress. A great anticlimax it seemed after the magnificent Sir Oliver Lodge and other overpowering press personalities. No imposing facade here, only a poor vulgar creature like myself.

We had a short chat about youth camps. I said these organisations appear to ignore sex. 'Oh well' he said, 'every Jack has his Jill', and that is all I

10 It seems that the Nazis held a grudge against Church for having secured the cash payment. In 1940 his name was listed, just above that of Winston Churchill, in the Black Book (*Sonderfahndungsliste G.B.*) of people who were to be immediately arrested if Germany occupied Britain in World War II. Baird Television Ltd. was among 171 companies listed for special investigation, linked with the name of Church. Baird himself was not named in the Black Book, but Isidore Ostrer (see Chapter 9) was.

11 Moseley had already been in New York several weeks earlier and had started negotiations with Donald Flamm on a jointly operated television station.*

12 By a further coincidence, the *Aquitania* was to end its life within a few miles of Helensburgh. It was broken up at Faslane, on the Gareloch, in 1950.

Baird meets his 'demi-god' H.G. Wells on the Aquitania, *October 1931. (Royal Television Society)*

remember of the conversation with my demigod. Mr. Knight however photographed us together on the boat deck.

As the ship approached New York harbour I was surprised to see on the pier a body of Highland pipers marching up and down with great elan to the skirl of the pipes. These wretched men proved to be a gang of comic opera pipers from the Ziegfeld Follies. A misguided but enthusiastic American publicity agent had arranged to give me a real Scottish reception. I was to walk in front of this procession, with a police escort, to my royal suite at the Waldorf Astoria. I could not face it. I slipped away and reached the hotel unobtrusively in a taxi; a few minutes later the Highlanders (from Czechoslovakia, Louisiana and Hollywood) arrived. It was an expensive matter pacifying them. The royal suite was overpowering, particularly the bathroom which was an enormous hall having a vast black marble bath set in the floor with a great profusion of sprays and showers and gilded W.C.s. The suite was filled with press men, photo bulbs flashing and reporters taking notes. Encouraged by the dynamo publicity man they stayed on but gave me the impression that they had no interest whatsoever in myself or my works and much preferred to concentrate on the whisky and refreshments. At two in the morning the last of them had reeled out or been carried out and I retired to my royal bed.

The next morning the roundabout started at 9 o'clock with three business visitors to join me at breakfast to discuss a very important proposition, which seemed to me incomprehensible nonsense, but the guests ate heartily and drank enormous quantities of rye whisky until at 11 a.m. one of them collapsed on the couch and lay as if dead with glazed eyes. The prohibition spirit had got him; he was removed for an application of the stomach-pump.

This seemed to be quite a commonplace part of business routine. More business men arrived, more press men. I had ten guests whom I had never seen or heard of before, to lunch. They talked incessantly. When I went to the W.C. they followed me still talking. At dinner time, two more arrived accompanied by their dames with a spare dame for my use. They stayed and stayed apparently with the intention of staying the night, dames and all. I wanted to do my best to be friendly and hospitable to everybody but these hard faced drunken pussies were the last straw. I told Knight if he did not clear them all out I would go to another hotel. He had them out in ten minutes; he was the soul of tact and determination.

Mayor Walker was Mayor of New York at the time of my visit, and it was arranged that he should welcome me to the City. I was conducted to the City Hall by a police escort, which consisted of four policemen mounted on motorcycles. One drove ahead of my car, the others went one on each side and one behind. All four of them made a terrible noise with the sirens with which they were equipped. When we arrived at the City Hall, a small band of Ziegfeld Follies Highlanders were marching up and down outside playing 'The Barren Rocks of Aden'. I was ushered into the Mayor's Parlour, and, after some little delay, Mayor Walker appeared, shook me cordially by the hand and then immediately began an address to the press representatives who were present in force. He evidently did this sort of thing regularly. 'We have with us here today', said the Mayor '…a man who has given us his world famous invention of—', here he hesitated for a moment and his secretary whispered in a stage whisper 'Television'. The Mayor then went on to give a dissertation chiefly on the wonders of New York, and kept referring to me as an Englishman, although there was a band of pipers outside. The proceedings came to a conclusion with cordial handshakes and the flash of press cameras, and I was driven to the Waldorf to a lunch of clam chowder soup (made from oysters) and roast jumbo squab (a small chicken).

While I was becoming thoroughly impatient with thirsty press men and futile agents I had my first meeting with American big business. Solomon Rossoff was an American millionaire.[13] I was told he was interested in our activities and likely to finance us if properly handled. Jacob Goldberg his lawyer arrived to see our demonstration and report to Rossoff. Goldberg was

13 'Solomon Rossoff' was Baird's misnomer for Samuel R. Rosoff, a wealthy construction contractor.*

the usual type of Jewish solicitor,[14] a little withered up man with beady eyes smoking a thin black cigar. Pockrass, our agent, who spoke his language, endeavoured to instil some enthusiasm into the cynical Goldberg as he watched our picture with an appearance of disinterested contempt and finally with an 'It ain't up to the pictures', took his departure. 'There's no pleasing that guy,' said Pockrass, 'If you was to show him Jesus Christ walking out of the garden of Eden he would say it was lousy.'

After a time I got my bearings, and, beginning to find my way about more or less, got down to some real business with Donald Flamm[15] the head of the WMCA, one of the big broadcasting stations in New York. After interminable negotiations, visits to Washington, giving evidence before committees, giving demonstrations with apparatus we had brought over and all sorts of excursions and alarms, we duly signed and sealed an agreement whereby WMCA. was to commence the broadcasting of television in New York using our apparatus upon terms satisfactory to all parties.

I then went to Washington to give evidence before the Wireless Committee,[16] for the purpose of securing permission for WMCA to broadcast television, and had my first experience of American legal methods. The complete lack of formality was astounding to one accustomed to the dignity and red tape of British procedure. Reporters, witnesses, solicitors and a smattering of the public sat all together in a large hall. The Commissioner proved to be a young man, I should think anything from 20 to 28 in appearance. He lay back in his chair gazing abstractedly at the ceiling, throughout the proceedings.

Everybody in the hall seemed to give evidence at interminable length. When my turn came the subject had been so thoroughly exhausted that there was little left for me to add; I did my best and the proceedings terminated without comment from the Commissioner.

Donald Flamm was, however, quite happy about it, and told me that we were certain to get permission. And he was right. WMCA got the necessary permit. Feeling that I had done a good bit of work I returned to London. We had obtained permission from the Radio Commission at Washington for our broadcasts and naturally thought we were all right.

14 This unfortunate remark would not have raised any eyebrows at the time it was written.

15 Donald Jason Flamm (1899–1998) was a leading figure in the American broadcasting industry and he later became one of the founders of the Voice of America. He always remembered Baird with admiration and affection and felt that he deserved more recognition in the USA. Flamm and Sydney Moseley tried unsuccessfully to persuade Baird to move to the USA in the early part of World War II.*

16 The body to which he gave evidence was the Federal Radio Commission, the precursor of the Federal Communications Commission.

The law in America however moves in a mysterious way, guided by the unseen finger of big business. Radio Corporation of America who did not want to see Baird broadcasting in New York now moved, and appealed through a nominee to the Federal Court. They asked that the decision of the Radio Commissioner be revoked and that we be prohibited from broadcasting television on the grounds that no foreign or foreign controlled company could be allowed to broadcast in the U.S.A. Their appeal was granted and our scheme fell through. The whole thing proved an utter loss. It was a most serious blow and the company was in bad trouble at home.

It might be asked why we could not sell our patents in the U.S.A. The answer is that the patent position in America is truly appalling, and quite hopeless for any foreigner. Whatever patents you may have can always be anticipated in America, for it is only necessary for your rivals to get up in a court of law, assuming of course they are American citizens, and swear that they thought about your invention on a date preceding the date on which you filed your patent. Then if they can produce witnesses, (a simple if expensive matter), to prove that they spoke of this and described it at that date, before the date of your patent, 'Priority of conception' is established and your patent becomes valueless.

The only way to get anything done in America is to sell out for what you can get to an American company, and let Americans fight Americans.

I arrived back in London to find an angry and impatient board awaiting me, and Moseley in control of the situation. I had stayed in New York some three months,[17] and the only business result of this activity was the contract with WMCA. There was one very much more important result however, as far as I was concerned, and that was my marriage which took place in New York on November 13th 1931. While this was, of course, a purely domestic matter[18] and had nothing to do with the board, I think it caused a certain amount of resentment. They subconsciously thought, perhaps, that I was using up the company's time for my personal affairs. Personally I think my marriage helped the negotiations, as there is nothing the American delights in more than a celebration of some sort. All our business concerns in New York were invited to a magnificent dinner to celebrate the occasion and they certainly appreciated it. I do not know if Mrs. Baird appreciated it equally.[19]

17 Baird had arrived in New York on 13 October; he and Margaret left on 18 December 1931 on the *Adriatic*.*

18 Baird's memoirs contain very little about his wife and children. Nevertheless he was a good father to Diana and me, and my mother was devoted to him (see Chapter 10).

19 Margaret Baird later said that, in the picture of the dinner, she and her new husband looked like 'a couple of sheep among a lot of wolves'.

Wedding dinner at the Half Moon Hotel, Coney Island, N.Y., November 15 1931. The line-up on the top table (from the left) is Donald Flamm and his first wife Rhoda, the Bairds, and Walter Knight. The other guests have not been identified.

What should have been a honeymoon was nothing but a succession of business engagements.

When I got back to London, the board was impatient to know the results of my lengthy stay in New York. I had the WMCA agreement to show them, but unfortunately within a matter of weeks came the news that the Federal Commission had turned down our application to broadcast. The whole deal was therefore off, and my visit to America from the business point of view had been entirely a waste of time. It had been an expensive waste of time also, not only for the company, but for myself, as there was such agitation over my expenses, led by Moseley, that I agreed to pay half out of my own pocket.

I had found to my cost, as Hutchinson had found some years earlier, the appalling difficulty of getting any definite business deal completed in the U.S.A.

Chapter Nine

The position in 1933 was that we had in hand about £50,000, our system was being regularly broadcast by the B.B.C., we were selling a number of receivers and had a monopoly of television in the British Isles. Our German company was also doing well. Apart from the precarious financial state of the company we had very good prospects. Television was going ahead rapidly, the use of the ultra short waves having opened out big possibilities.

Rivals had appeared in the field, the Marconi Company having staged a demonstration at the British Association in Leicester, and the H.M.V. Company[1] having also given a demonstration at the Physical Society meeting in 1931. Both these companies had however shown the now obsolescent mirror drum apparatus. We alone had shown high definition cathode ray pictures.

The Marconi Company got in touch with us in 1932. They were anxious to join forces; I went up to Chelmsford and was shown round their television research department. Many more meetings and lunches followed and the whole stage was set for a merger.[2] Our cash, however, was getting short. We had introduced television to the B.B.C. and instead of their paying us (as the Germans did) we paid them for the use of their transmitter.

The money we got from the sale of television receivers was little compared to our outgoings and it was obvious that some time must still elapse before we could become a paying concern. The controlling shares were held by Television Ltd., and this company had been put into voluntary liquidation. One night, going home with Moseley to his house on Primrose Hill, I suggested that he should get some of his financial friends together and buy Television Ltd., from the Receiver. The seed took root and Sydney got busy; by what devious financial wizardry it was accomplished, I have never been able to follow, but by some succession of obscure financial somersaults Moseley

1 'His Master's Voice' was the trade label used on records produced by the Gramophone Company, an American company which was also loosely known as H.M.V. In April 1931, this company had merged with the Columbia Graphophone (*sic*) Company to form Electrical and Musical Industries Ltd. (E.M.I.).* However, Baird continued to refer to E.M.I. in his memoirs as 'the H.M.V. Company'.

2 Hardly anything can be found on record about merger negotiations between the Baird and Marconi companies. It seems that these negotiations were verbal and therefore informal.*

got his friends to put up the money and he himself got possession of Television Ltd.[3] He did not write 'Money making in Stocks and Shares' without knowing his subject.

The control did not remain long in Moseley's hands. In a matter of weeks it had passed to Gaumont British, or in effect into the hands of Isidore Ostrer[4] who held control of the great Gaumont British combine. He was totally unlike any other successful business man I have ever met. I liked him but never felt at home in his company. I was, even if indirectly, in the position of an employee and when I did see him I invariably had some axe to grind. These influences served to destroy freedom of conversation. There was always an undercurrent of uneasy alertness. I was on guard all the time and unable to speak freely.

The Receiver had sold out Television Ltd. to Moseley for £15,000. Out of this I finally got £3,000, it was all I received for my shares of which I never sold one, although at one time my holding was worth nearly a quarter of a million.

If an inventor reads this book, let him by this be admonished to do what Graham Bell (the inventor of the telephone) did, and sell at once for cash. Inventors are no match for financiers where stocks and shares are concerned and will, if they hold on, find that the financiers have the cash and they have the paper.

Isidore Ostrer immediately put his own representatives on the Board; Sir Harry Greer, a well-known City figure (Chairman of Stephens Inks and interested in many other companies) and a Mr. Clayton, a clever accountant. After two meetings with some unpleasantness between Sir Harry and Baron Ampthill, the Baron sent a letter to the secretary saying that owing to pressure of other matters he would be unable to continue with the company and with great regret would have to leave us. Sir Harry then took the chair. Before Sir Harry came on the Board we had commenced negotiations with the Marconi Company for a merger and these had reached an advanced stage. If this merger had been completed it would have been, in my opinion, greatly to our advantage. The Marconi people were very keen and little but drawing up of the agreement remained to be done; they had shown us over their research laboratories, there had been a succession of meetings with Sydney in the forefront; it looked as if it would go through. But in the course of many unpleasant scenes at board meetings, the new directors turned on me. Everything I had done

3 In his 1952 biography of Baird, Moseley devotes an entire chapter to this episode. See next footnote.

4 Isidore Ostrer (1889–1975), who had been at school with Sydney Moseley, personally authorised a loan of £5800 to Moseley to help him acquire Television Ltd. from the Receiver. Baird was unaware of this.

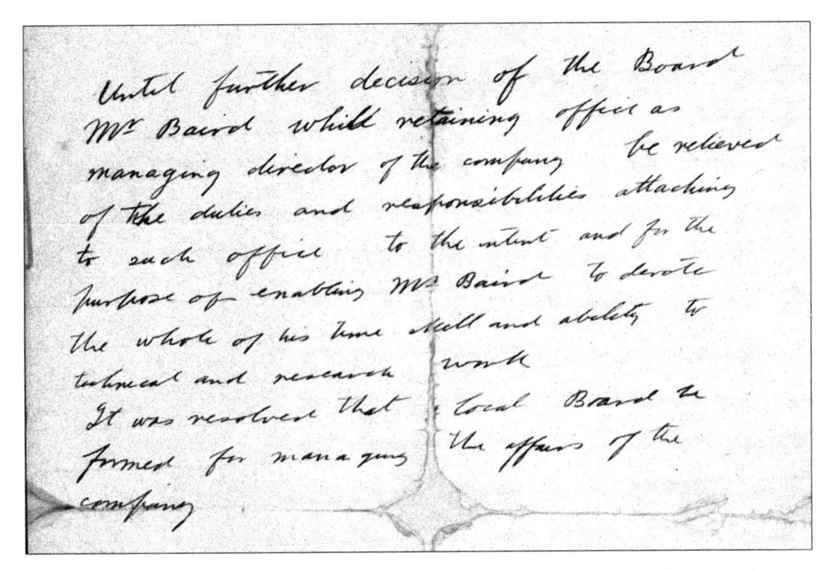

Until further decision of the Board
Mr Baird whilst retaining office as
managing director of the company be relieved
of the duties and responsibilities attaching
to such office to the intent and for the
purpose of enabling Mr Baird to devote
the whole of his time skill and ability to
technical and research work
It was resolved that a local Board be
formed for managing the affairs of the
company

'...In the course of many unpleasant scenes at board meetings, the new directors turned on me.' Baird copied down the exact wording of the decision in June 1933 to relieve him of executive duties.

had been wrong. Daniel in the lion's den was a poor show compared with Baird in the Baird board room!

Two more directors were brought on the Board to replace Moseley[5] and Baron Ampthill and incidentally to cut the ground even more from under my feet. One of the new directors was an old employee of the Company whom Moseley and I had sacked.[6] The other was Captain A.G.D. West.[7] He and Church visited Berlin and saw all that was being done there in television. On his return West sent in a lengthy report. This was extremely favourable to myself and the work I had been doing, and stated that I had provided all the essentials of an entirely successful television system and my results were at least equal to the best he had seen in Germany; all that was needed was steady and energetic development. This was a bad blow to my critics. West and I got on well and in fact he was my chief supporter on the board. Now our headquarters were in south London and I had my own private laboratory at my home[8] where I did research with my own staff independent of the general

5 Ostrer had eased Moseley off the board after a bitter row between Moseley and Greer over the ending of the Marconi merger negotiations.

6 This was Captain Jarrard, who had been in charge of the American company.*

7 West had moved to Baird Television Ltd. from a post with Associated Talking Pictures at their Ealing studios.*

8 Baird's house was at 3 Crescent Wood Road, near the Crystal Palace where the company had its laboratories and ultra-short wave transmitter.

'West was …my chief supporter on the board.' Baird with Capt. A.G.D. West at the British Association Meeting in Leicester, September 1933. (Prof. Richard West)

work of the company.[9] I was able to show some good results and, after a time, the crisis died down and the bitter attacks of my co-directors became infrequent and ultimately died away.

The position when West came into the company was that we had developed a 120-line cathode ray system which was, I believe, better than anything our rivals in this country had to offer. In any case it was far superior to the show given by the Marconi Company at the British Association meeting in Leicester. Their exhibit consisted of a 50 line mirror drum apparatus, while our apparatus showed a 120 line picture on a cathode ray tube giving greatly superior definition. It was also far in advance of the mirror drum apparatus shown by the H.M.V. Company at the Physical Society's exhibition.

The first catastrophic thing to happen after the alterations on the board was the termination of the negotiations with the Marconi Company. Who was chiefly responsible for this very foolish rebuff I do not know; the final step

9 Baird's first assistant at Crescent Wood Road was Paul Reveley, whose reminiscences of those days played an important part in the 2002 television documentary 'JLB—The Man Who Saw the Future'.

was certainly taken by Isidore Ostrer. I had nothing to do with it and thoroughly disapproved; it was all done over my head.

The Marconi Company were not, however, the only big concern interested in our activities. Lord Hirst, head of the G.E.C. combine, was a friend of Major Church and was very interested in our company. Shortly after Gaumont British had acquired control, and after we had turned down the Marconi Company, we got in close touch with G.E.C. and they were anxious to form an alliance with us in television. The immense importance of such a tie-up was very obvious to me, but it was not so obvious to the other members of the board and, although we got as far as having regular technical meetings, with our two research departments working together in unison, and although the G.E.C. were anxious for an agreement with us, at the very last minute Isidore Ostrer stepped in and turned G.E.C. down. I was very upset about this, but not so upset as Major Church, from whose efforts this very important alliance had so nearly taken place.

Major Church, however, continued with the company, although but for our close personal friendship he would have resigned in protest. It was due to Major Church's efforts that I received an Honorary Fellowship of the Royal Society of Edinburgh.[10] This distinction, which is limited to twenty-two British Scientists of 'outstanding distinction' was a very gratifying honour.

While these business upheavals were in progress our research work was going ahead. We were progressing with the transmission of ultra short waves and were, I think, ahead of anyone, certainly in England.

In the early days I had been continually concerned with the problem of getting more detail into a television picture. Transmission at that time was on the medium waves, that is to say the ordinary waves used by the B.B.C. for transmitting sound, and these do not permit of more than a very limited amount of detail being seen in the picture; it was this that limited the picture to 30 lines.[11]

In 1932 we were doing experiments with ultra short waves, and I remember discussing this while lunching with Professor Appleton.[12] He stressed the

10 Baird was elected Honorary F.R.S.E. on 5 July 1937.* At the same meeting, the quantum physicist Max Planck was elected.

11 The layperson may find it confusing that short radio waves accommodate more picture lines than medium waves. However, the radio frequency varies inversely with wavelength; short wave signals have a higher frequency which enables more detailed signals to be carried.

12 Professor Sir Edward V. Appleton (1892–1965) was awarded the Nobel Prize in Physics in 1947 for his use of reflected radio waves to study the ionosphere. In 1931–32 he had been brought in by Baird Television Ltd. as a paid consultant. He strongly recommended that television should be broadcast by ultra-short waves which allowed high definition pictures to be sent.*

importance of this work very strongly and advised me to push ahead and give a demonstration at the earliest possible moment, so that on the 29th April, 1932, we gave a demonstration from our ultra short wave transmitter at Long Acre, the images being received on a 30-line television receiver on the roof of Selfridges. That was the first public demonstration of ultra short wave television given, so far as I know, in the world, but certainly in this country. No doubt other people were working on ultra short waves, but by giving a demonstration we established and drew attention to their possibilities in television.

By 1933 the development of the ultra short wave had proceeded to such an extent that it was possible to show scenes having very much greater detail than was possible over the ordinary B.B.C. channels. We gave a demonstration to the British Association meeting at Leicester. We also gave a whole series of demonstrations from the Crystal Palace on ultra short wavelength of 8.5 metres, our receivers being located at Film House in Wardour Street in the centre of London.

We were, however, by this time faced with the competition of several other companies. The H.M.V. Company approached the B.B.C. with a rival television system. No details were published but I believe it was some form of mirror drum giving a picture of 150 lines. The B.B.C. were negotiating with them and we also had put forward our high definition system. This consisted of a development on the 30 line apparatus, a disc revolving at very high speed perforated with holes arranged in a spiral, causing a light spot to traverse the person being transmitted. This was used on close-ups and gave very good results. For outdoor scenes we used what is known as the intermediate film process, that is to say we photographed the scene to be transmitted with a cinematograph camera.[13] Through an elaborate arrangement of developing tanks, this film was developed in a matter of seconds. The film was then televised, a revolving perforated disc being used for scanning. This rather elaborate process was necessary as we could not get enough light direct from the scene itself. By using a film we could use the light from an arc lamp direct through the film on to the photo electric cell.

Later we experimented with a camera of the electronic type,[14] and had one of these installed at the B.B.C., but it was not sufficiently sensitive to compete with the Iconoscope.

13 The initial development of the intermediate film process had been done by Fernseh A.G. Most of the early German television programmes were produced in this way.

14 This was the image dissector camera developed in the U.S.A. by Philo Farnsworth (1906–1971). His work was ignored for many years because of the bitter rivalry between him and R.C.A., but he is now being recognised in the U.S.A. R.C.A. is being criticised for its treatment of Farnsworth.

A rare domestic snapshot of Baird at his house in Crescent Wood Road with his children Diana and Malcolm, spring 1936.

It was agreed by the B.B.C. that they would test our new television apparatus and give it a three-months trial on the understanding that we would remove our apparatus by the 1st January, 1934, as the H.M.V. Company claimed to have ready apparatus which they also wished to install for test by the B.B.C. We duly installed our apparatus and commenced demonstrations, showing pictures with 120 lines, and as we had agreed, we removed it at the end of the trial period so that the space would be available for the H.M.V. Company. They, however, did not install their apparatus.

The position became increasingly complicated by the demands of other companies to have their system investigated.

The television situation had now become so important and complex that again a Television Committee was formed by Parliament to investigate the whole situation. Again Sir William Mitchell-Thompson, now Lord Selsdon, was chairman. The committee were finally unable to choose between our apparatus and the apparatus of Marconi-E.M.I.[15] We had a system of 240 lines; Marconi-E.M.I. had adopted a 405 line system of scanning developed

15 In May 1934, the Marconi and E.M.I. companies formed a jointly owned subsidiary company, Marconi-E.M.I. Television Ltd., under the chairmanship of Lord Inverforth. Its sole aim was to develop high-definition television.*

by R.C.A. and described in a patent taken out by Ballard, one of their assistants. They also used as a transmitter an apparatus called an Iconoscope, developed by the research department of R.C.A. headed by Zworykin. We showed a better transmission of cinematograph films and close-ups, but our intermediate film was a clumsy and inefficient device compared to the Iconoscope.

As far as actual results went there was little or nothing to choose between us. We could show better cinema transmission; Marconi-E.M.I. were better on outdoor work, but, taken altogether, their merits were about equal. This, indeed proved to be also the opinion of the committee who, being unable to decide on one or the other, recommended that both systems be tried by the B.B.C. for a period of two years, after which one or the other should be adopted at the B.B.C.'s discretion.

The opening ceremony[16] of the high definition system was transmitted by both systems, first the Baird system and then the Marconi-E.M.I. system. All the notabilities in any way connected with television appeared on the platform and were televised, all except Mr. Baird, who was not invited but sat in considerable anger and disgust in the body of the hall among the rank and file. Thus is pioneer work recognized. This little episode was but another addition to the host of slights and insults given to me by the B.B.C. What the devil had they done for television? But there they sat sunning themselves in the limelight as the men responsible for this great achievement, for so they apparently wished to appear. And I, the best part of whose life had been given to television, who had transmitted the first television image ever seen, who had first introduced television to the B.B.C., who, year after year, had forced the pace and pushed Britain and the B.B.C. into the position of leadership—I sat snubbed and humiliated among the audience! Such was the nature of my thoughts as I returned to my abode.

Now we were faced at last with really serious competition. We had against us the whole resources of the vast R.C.A. combine, comprising not only the biggest companies in the U.S.A. but the great Telefunken Company in Germany and a host of others. If we had joined Marconi we would have been with this combine, not against it. Our policy of facing the world single-handed was sheer insanity.

While we and Marconi-E.M.I. were competing in the B.B.C. we received a severe and unexpected setback.[17] For many years I had considered the

16 This opening ceremony took place on 2 November 1936. In the variety programme which followed, the musical comedy actress Adele Dixon sang a special song which started with these florid words: 'A mighty maze/of mystic, magic rays/is all about us in the blue,/and in sight and sound they trace/living pictures out of space/to bring our new wonder to you.'

17 The nature of this setback is explained three paragraphs further on!

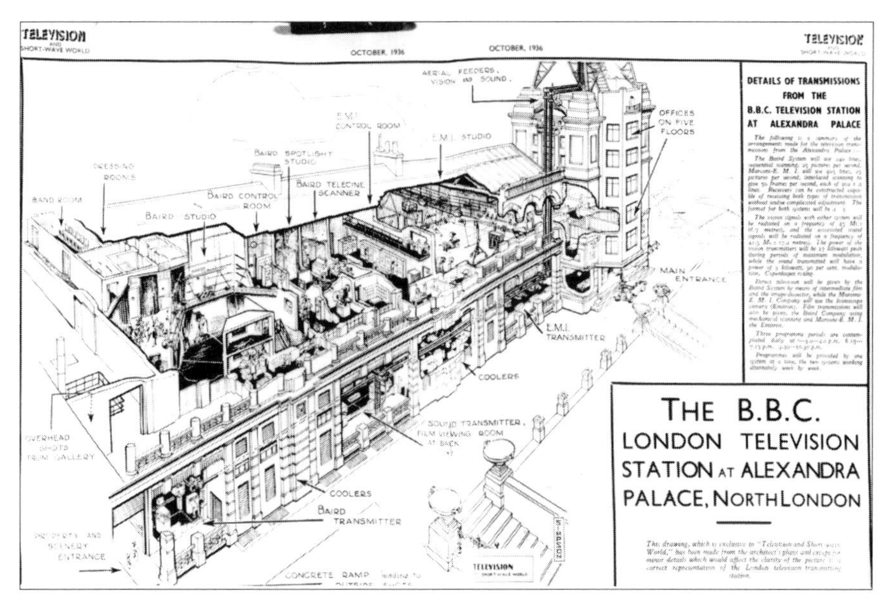

Layout of the competing Baird and Marconi-E.M.I. systems at Alexandra Palace in October 1936. (Royal Television Society)

possibility of using one of the towers of the Crystal Palace as an aerial for ultra short wave transmissions. So, in 1933, when the need for larger premises arose, this dream came true. We moved our laboratory to the Crystal Palace and also started our factory there, coming to an arrangement with Sir Henry Buckland to take over the South Tower and an extensive part of the Palace buildings. There we erected and tested the whole of the transmission plant which we supplied to the B.B.C. for an ultra short wave transmission.

In the old days we had, in Long Acre, our own studio and our own broadcasting and had, in effect, a rival broadcasting system to the B.B.C., with our own independent programmes being received by the public. This came to an end when the B.B.C. took us over and I often regretted this and thought that we would have been better to have continued independently. When we took part of the Crystal Palace and erected our own station, this opportunity again arose. I began transmitting television pictures from the South Tower of the Crystal Palace to the screen of the Dominion Theatre, Tottenham Court Road. For a few weeks we showed pictures in monochrome and we gave a demonstration to the audience there of a transmission of television in colour on a twelve foot screen, the first time this had ever been done. This transmission was by wireless and to a public audience and, strictly speaking, illegal, but no objection was raised. The same contention of illegality might have been raised against our early transmissions from Long Acre, but in neither case was any effort made by the authorities to stop us. I was very anxious that we should develop this transmission and begin our own transmissions to cinemas. The board, however, were divided on this question and certain members felt that we should drop the transmission side altogether, leaving it to the B.B.C., so that with disagreement on the board nothing was done. While our transmitter was still functioning in our own hands we gave a rather spectacular and amusing demonstration.

At our general meeting, the chairman, Sir Harry Greer, went to the Crystal Palace and televised his speech from there to the hall in Wardour Street where the general meeting was being held. Some hundred shareholders saw him on the screen erected on the platform of the hall and listened to his speech spoken from the Crystal Palace. This was a startling innovation and may prove popular with chairmen in the future when they have to address rowdy meetings!

While the tests of our apparatus in competition with the Marconi-E.M.I. were in progress, a terrible disaster befell us. One evening, when I was in the middle of dinner, the telephone rang and a wildly excited voice informed me that the Crystal Palace was on fire! My house, 3 Crescent Wood Road, is less than a mile from the Palace and, looking from the window after the 'phone call, I saw a red glow in the sky. I at once rushed out, hatless and in slippers, and ran towards the Palace. Long before I reached it the road was completely blocked with motor cars and a dense crowd of people. I managed to elbow my way through to the front of the Palace, which by this time was a seething mass of flames—a wonderful spectacle!

In the fire we lost nearly £100,000 worth of apparatus. True, a good deal of the value of this was recovered from insurance, but the immense disorganization, loss of time and loss of valuable records were irreplaceable. This disaster also occurred at the most awkward possible time[18] and seriously interfered with the transmissions with our apparatus from the B.B.C. Spare parts and apparatus which we were about to install were destroyed in the fire.

However, the fight was not yet over, and had my friend Sydney been with us, I think we might well have won, combine or no combine. As it was we had the leadership of a chairman with no grasp whatever of the situation, backed by an unimaginative and uninterested board. West himself was immensely energetic, but a child in a situation of this sort, which needed the craft of a Machiavelli. As for myself, I at least had realized the position, but had not the ear of Isidore Ostrer, the one man who controlled our destinies, and without that I was impotent. My co-directors, with the exception of Major Church, disregarded me, and Church was as impotent as I was. Isidore

18 The Crystal Palace fire took place on 30 November 1936.

Ostrer would listen only to West and Clayton, and they told him everything was rosy and the outlook sure, that the Marconi-E.M.I. had no chance.

For the allotted period, the Baird and Marconi-E.M.I. systems were transmitted on alternate weeks. The public could receive either system on the same receiver.

Then came a bitter blow—the B.B.C. adopted the Marconi system. And so, after all these years, we were put out of the B.B.C. The fact that it was the R.C.A. system imported from the U.S.A., that the scanning used was covered by the R.C.A.-Ballard Patent and the transmitter was the Iconoscope of Zworykin and the R.C.A. research department, did not hinder the Marconi-E.M.I. combine from proclaiming the system as all-British.[19] The Iconoscope was now called the Emitron. Ballard was ignored, and in an amazingly short time the Marconi publicity department had established it in the public mind that Marconi invented television. The public is like a very deaf and slow witted old gentleman, and has neither the time nor the inclination to analyse facts. All that reached to its consciousness was the continual trumpeting of the Marconi publicity—'Marconi Television, Marconi Television'. Poor Marconi was dead and buried and when alive he never knew one end of a television apparatus from the other. The first time he ever saw television was in my laboratory. However, the Marconi publicity department, aided by the great army of scientific consultants and myrmidons of this huge combine, naturally did all they could to snub, belittle and ignore my work. With tentacles everywhere, they succeeded in a way which left me mouthing with impotent wrath. The success of their work was brought home to me when I overheard a conversation over the 'phone between an elderly lady (who I thought knew all about me) and a friend—'Yes! We have Mr. Baird staying with us', silence, then, 'You know! Mr. Baird, the Television Scientist', silence—the friend did not know! 'Oh! You must know, he invented a television nearly as good as Marconi's!'

I struggled all I could in vain. My squeaks went unheeded. I was the first person in the world to see by television. The evidence is overwhelming. But the Marconi megaphone merely continued its trumpeting 'Marconi Television'—'Marconi, Marconi, Marconi!' And so, at length my ineffectual protests were heard no more. I was the first person to see by television, before my demonstration only shadows had been sent. But the host of scientists employed by

19 Baird always maintained that the Marconi-E.M.I. electronic system was simply a modification of the R.C.A. system. Marconi-E.M.I. vehemently insisted that their system was an independent all-British achievement. However, when David Sarnoff, head of R.C.A., introduced television to Americans at the New York World Fair in 1939, he made no mention of either Marconi-E.M.I. or Baird.

The Baird Television Athletic Club annual dinner-dance took place on 18 March 1938 while the Bairds were on their way to Australia. The group includes Mr and Mrs H. Clayton (1, 2); Sir Harry and Lady Greer (3, 4); Captain and Mrs West (5, 6); Captain W.J. Jarrard (7). Gwen Clapp (8) is in the front row while the self-effacing Ben Clapp (9) is near the back. The menu included 'Push-Poularde de Baird en Cathovisorolle.' (Alexandra Palace Television Society)

the Marconi-E.M.I.-R.C.A. combine are not going to hand out any bouquets to possible rivals, so they ignore my work.[20]

To be thrown out of the B.B.C. after all these years of pioneer work, to be displaced by newcomers, was to me a bitter blow. Clayton and Greer did not seem to appreciate this. 'I can't understand,' said Clayton, 'Why you place such importance on this transmission. After all, the money is in the sale of receivers. I understand, of course, that from the sentimental angle it must be a blow to you. If you will pardon me speaking freely, it hurts your vanity. But simply looking at the thing as a business man from a purely business

20 The 'anti-Baird' campaign was still under way in November 1966 when the B.B.C. showed a documentary film called 'The Discovery of Television', to mark the 30th anniversary of its high definition service. It featured interviews with many former Marconi-E.M.I. employees and ended with presenter Derek Hart solemnly intoning that 'John Logie Baird did not invent television.' The B.B.C. gave a copy of the 16 mm film to my mother who by this time had moved to South Africa. She never bothered to watch it.

angle, I think that it's the best thing that could have happened. We have done nothing but lose money in transmission. Now we can leave it to the B.B.C. and concentrate on the receiver market'.

Before the B.B.C. ultimately adopted the Marconi-EMI system they purchased our apparatus from us as this was part of the agreement. I was sorry that events developed in this way as otherwise I should have cherished hopes that we might start an independent television broadcasting system. But the sale of the apparatus to the B.B.C. made this impossible.

It seemed to me that now, being out of the B.B.C., we should concentrate on television for the cinema and should work hand-in-glove with Gaumont British, installing screens in their cinemas and working towards the establishment of a broadcasting company independent of the B.B.C. for the supply of television programmes to cinemas. I reported this view to the board, but it was brushed aside. However, in my little laboratory at Sydenham, within narrow limits I had a free hand and had built up a big screen and projector. This with Ostrer's consent had been installed in the Dominion Cinema, so that some sort of start had been made. The B.B.C. decision was a blow to Ostrer, and he was thoroughly dissatisfied and even hinting of withdrawing his support from the company when, by a heaven-sent opportunity, I was thrown in contact with him at the Television Exhibition at the Science Museum. I was filled to exploding point with enthusiasm for cinema television, and let him have it in full force.

Ostrer, when once one had established contact, was very impressionable and he rose at once. We had tea together and discussed the position at length. 'Some vital personality is needed to force this thing through', he said, 'the present board contains no one with the requisite personality and driving force. We need fresh blood. It will be a big fight—we need a fighter.' Several names were mentioned and then the name I had been waiting for, Sydney A. Moseley. We parted on intimate terms. I was back in the picture. I wasted no time. I pushed forward my plans and, working all day and most of the night, was able to give a demonstration at the Dominion a few weeks later. To this came Ostrer, anxious to see me. We had a long talk and he arranged to get in touch with Moseley forthwith.

A few days later, to the utter dismay of the other members of the board, Ostrer appeared at the Crystal Palace accompanied by the arch villain Sydney. Here was the man whom the whole board had been reviling, being shown round and consulted by the deity himself, who obviously had it in his mind to place this unmitigated rascal in a dominant position in the Company. It was one of the few occasions I have seen Clayton look thoroughly upset. 'Good Lord!' he said to me, 'do you know who Ostrer is bringing with him?

Moseley,' and then realizing that I did not quite share his outlook, 'Oh! I suppose you know all about it.'

The situation ripened nicely. A little private meeting followed at which Moseley, Ostrer, myself and West were present. We had a happy little meeting. It was decided to form a new company, Cinema-Television, which would virtually control Baird Television; Moseley to be a director of this new company and given wide powers, including what would have amounted to control of Greer and Clayton and the others. I wanted the word Baird in the name of the new company, but the others thought that, if the whole cinema industry was to be embraced, it was better—for the start anyhow—to have a perfectly general and all-embracing title. I gave way unwillingly.

This Company was duly formed with a nominal capital of £250,000. Ostrer and Moseley were now united in brotherly love and close communication, causing much snorting and gnashing of teeth among the other faction. They dissembled their grief, however, and greeted Moseley as the long lost brother.

Moseley was to come again on the board of Baird Television Ltd. as well as being on the board of Cinema Television, and there was to be a reorganization of the Baird board. I was to become President (at £4,000 per annum), Greer was to remain Chairman and Clayton, Managing Director. I had some experience of the way arrangements of this sort fell through if not pressed, and I insisted on getting my new contract at once. Moseley, for some obscure reason, did not insist on coming on the Baird board at once, but agreed to come on after our general meeting. By this delay he lost the opportunity. The other members of the board, except myself, were determined to keep him out and used the delay to raise barriers and convince Ostrer that Moseley was 'better off the board than on.' I think, however, if he would have joined the board the course of events would have been very different. I believe we might have saved the company from catastrophe in spite of the war had we had his live and vivid intelligence and personality to help us in that crisis. But unfortunately at the time when I might, by pressing the matter, have got him on the board, I was invited to address a great Radio Convention which was being held in Australia.[21]

The Australian Government were to pay all expenses and our representatives in Sydney considered it a heaven-sent opportunity for opening out in that country. It had originally been intended by the convention to have Marconi, but his death left a vacant place and I was chosen as a substitute. I had some doubts about leaving London. The chance of visiting Australia was, however, too good to be missed, and so on the 22nd of February, 1938, I set sail with my wife from Marseilles on the *Strathaird*.

21 In 1938 Australia was celebrating its 150th anniversary with great enthusiasm.

Of the voyage there is little worth recounting. The plain statement of the ports visited, florid accounts of the wonders of the tropical seas, of the black hordes of India, and such like, are better done in guide books.

One episode, however, stands out in my memory. We had an agreement with an Indian syndicate which had acquired our television rights for India. This led to our becoming the guests of H.R.H. the Maharajah of Kutch when we reached Bombay. What a meal! All other banquets pale before it! Dish followed dish, delicious and exotic. I ate heartily and was horribly ill for nearly a week afterwards. In fact, we had reached Perth in Australia before my internal organs had got back to normal.

Mr. Bean, who represented our Australian interests and who had been responsible for fixing up my visit, met the ship at Perth. He had arranged for me to speak at a lunch to the Perth Radio Society. Professor Ross of Perth University[22] also met me, and Perth and Fremantle were explored and exhibited to us from his car—a beautiful place with a beautiful climate and one boon which, to me, raised Australia to a unique position. There were no natives; no filthy Arab beggars, as in North Africa, no indolent negroes as in the West Indies, no swarms of wretched poverty-stricken blacks, as in Bombay. But the people were such people as we find at home, road sweepers included.

In one of the many social Utopias which I have heard of, it has been proposed that no man's income should exceed £1,000 per annum; beyond which figure income tax would be 100%; also that the establishment of an idle aristocracy should be prevented by 100% death duties; and that by means of state assistance the community should eliminate extremes of poverty.

In Australia this appeared to me to have been already approximately reached. I saw no acute poverty and no 'slums' as we understand that term; on the other hand I saw no evidence of flaunting wealth, and found indeed an almost startling absence of anything in the nature of class distinctions. It was a country entirely inhabited by petty bourgeoisie and as I myself belong to that class I felt pleasantly at home. It reminded me of what the U.S.A. might become if it could be purged of its gangsters, its crooks, its horrible film magnates and upstart millionaires and all its strident, screaming vulgarity. I hope Australia will be allowed to develop in peace along its own lines. They seemed to me the happiest, healthiest and most sane common sense community which I have ever visited.

22 Baird refers to Perth University but he meant the University of Western Australia. Professor A.D. Ross held the chair of Physics there and had studied at Glasgow University at about the same time that Baird was at the Royal Technical College. They may have known each other from those days.

Baird addressing the World Radio Convention in Sydney, 6 April 1938. On the table is a cathode ray tube (The Cathovisor TM) manufactured by Baird Television Ltd.

I was given a splendid reception at Sydney and the Press (with a little nursing) rose to the occasion and, in fact, gave me such publicity as, in the words of a letter Mr. Bean afterwards wrote to the Board 'had never previously been accorded to any visitor to Australia, not even to the most distinguished royalty'.[23] At Sydney University I delivered my carefully prepared address to an enthusiastic audience. Sir Ernest Fisk, who was president of the Radio Society, I think was just a trifle upset by the amount of publicity the president of a rival concern was receiving and, in proposing the vote of thanks, took the opportunity to himself to make a lengthy speech stressing the Marconi-E.M.I. work[24] and arousing just a shade of impatience among the audience. Other speakers followed and the discussion concluded with a speech

23 Baird presented the Australians with one of his company's television sets, a large floor model known as the T5. It is now kept at the Museum Victoria in Melbourne, cherished as the first cathode-ray television receiver in the southern hemisphere.

24 Sir Ernest Fisk (1886–1965) was at this time chairman of Amalgamated Wireless (Australasia) Ltd. which had strong links with the Marconi company. Between 1945 and 1952 he was managing director of E.M.I.

from Mr. Bean, the vice-president—'We have argued like doctors and like doctors we have disagreed…'. The proceedings terminated and, accompanied by Sir Ernest Fisk and Lady Fisk, we returned to supper at the Hotel Australia.

So the visit to Australia came to an end, and we found ourselves back again on the *Strathaird* which had become by this time a second home. I thought the life on board ship ideal and would willingly have continued cruising through these tropical waters indefinitely, but soon we were back in Marseilles and soon after that I was sitting again at that board room table—'Gentlemen, is it your pleasure that I sign these minutes!' And so on.

The machine ran round with little apparent change. But behind the scene Moseley's goose had been well and thoroughly cooked. He had not only been kept off the board of Baird Television Ltd., but was out of favour with Ostrer and was fuming and fretting. Isidore Ostrer adopted his usual tactics and became absolutely inaccessible, but in Moseley he had met one of his own kidney, 'a goosehawk able to rend well his foe'.[25] Moseley got to work with his solicitors. He demanded a list of all the shareholders—to which he was legally entitled—and gave intimation to the secretary that at the next general meeting he intended to oppose the passing of the accounts and to demand a committee of enquiry. This made Ostrer sit up and take notice. He was already in serious trouble with his Gaumont British Company, which was being made the subject of a Board of Trade enquiry. The prospect of another Committee, headed by the formidable Sydney, was not one to be brushed aside. He capitulated; Moseley received a handsome contract with a promise of a future seat on the board and this, that and the other. These promises might or might not materialize, but the contract and the cash were fixed firmly by Moseley's lawyer there and then.

The work went on. We continued producing and selling receivers. Big screens were installed in several Gaumont cinemas. The Boon-Danahar boxing match and other topical events were shown to enthusiastic audiences on the television screen. I showed my own particular work—colour television—on a large screen at the Dominion Theatre and, just before War broke out, showed colour television on a small receiver[26] using a cathode ray tube and foreshadowing the time when colour television would replace monochrome

25 This is a slight variation on a line from Dante's *Inferno*: '…a goshawk able to rend well his foe'.

26 Colour was achieved by means of a transparent wheel, with segments in each of the primary colours, spinning rapidly in front of the cathode-ray tube which showed an alternating sequence of pictures for each colour. A somewhat similar technique was being developed independently in the U.S.A. by Dr Peter Goldmark of the Columbia Broadcasting System. In 1944 Baird devised a more advanced cathode-ray tube, the Telechrome, which did not require the coloured wheel (see Chapter 10).

The Bairds at St Tropez in April 1939, their last holiday before the war.

in the home. We had a monopoly of colour television and, personally, I thought it of great importance, although several of my co-directors were not so enthusiastic.

The Radio Show opened in August with the threat of war growing ever more ominous. We had, however, a first class exhibit and the show held on almost until war was declared. But finally the tension became impossible and the show closed. Almost immediately after, war was declared and the whole industry came to a complete standstill.

When war broke out Baird Television Limited was just rounding the corner after many ups and downs. We had orders pending to fit the Gaumont British cinemas with large screens, and our home receivers were considered the best on the market and were booming in great demand. Orders were pouring in. Our stores were stocked with receivers and we had a staff of nearly 500 men. Television was coming into its own! As soon as war was declared, every order was cancelled as the B.B.C. immediately stopped transmitting television

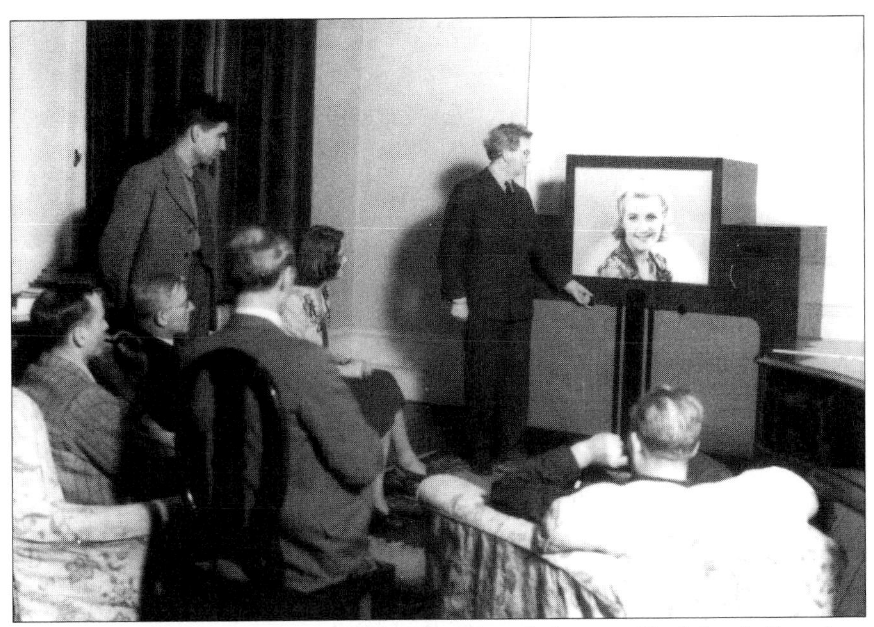

High-definition colour television demonstrated at 3 Crescent Wood Road, December 1940. (Ray Herbert)

and there was, therefore, nothing to receive. Television receivers became simply useless junk.

The Gaumont British held some £300,000 in bonds in the company, the total capital of the company being £1,080,000. Shortly after war was declared, these bond holders, under the terms of their bond, appointed receivers and ultimately put the company into liquidation, acquiring the company's assets in payment of their bonds. These assets were taken over by Cinema Television,[27] a company owned and controlled by Gaumont British.[28] In the meantime, as my contract terminated with the appointment of a receiver, I became a free agent.

I was in the middle of some extremely interesting and, I believed, important work on colour television and, rather than see this stopped, I continued it at my own expense, keeping on two assistants and working in a private laboratory attached to my house at 3 Crescent Wood Road. I also sent my name in to the authorities and expected to be approached with some form of government work, but no such offer materialized.[29] In the meantime, the

27 Cinema Television Ltd., later known as Cintel, remained in operation throughout the war under the technical direction of Captain West. The company was entirely dedicated to military work, including the manufacture of cathode-ray tubes for radar screens.

28 Gaumont British, including Cintel, was taken over by J. Arthur Rank in 1942. Isidore Ostrer had moved to the U.S.A. after the outbreak of war.

29 Although Baird himself was excluded from government work during the war, many junior employees of Baird Television Ltd. went into war-related fields like radar.

colour television made very good progress and I was able to show a 600-line colour picture of very fine quality and suitable for broadcasting through the B.B.C. with very little alteration to their existing apparatus. With the European war raging, however, nothing could be done. My only hope was that I should be able to keep going until after the war.

In the meantime a very sad event occurred. One blazing hot day in August[30] I was sitting basking in the sun in the garden at 3 Crescent Wood Road, hoping that no air raids would arrive, when I was handed a letter. Dear Sir... I could not for a moment realize it. Mephy, whom I had just written to and had arranged to visit, dead! Suicide! Impossible—why should he commit suicide? Why, without one hint or indication had he suddenly taken this irrevocable step out of everything? The finality, the tragic terrible loss that could never be replaced, struck me with brutal force. I was filled with hopeless regrets—why did I not go over to Ryde sooner? I could have stopped it. Why did I not write earlier? He never received my last letter, it was delivered the day after his death. Poor Mephy! Ryde, being opposite Portsmouth, had been having continual air raid alarms. He could not sleep and his nervous system must have given way completely.

My whole position was becoming very distressing. I had not only been badly hit financially but I had been in bad health for some time and the continual air raids, which had blown out the windows of my house and brought down all the ceilings, were very upsetting.

I decided to have a short holiday outside London and I went to an hotel which also advertised medical treatment,[31] with the intention of resting for a fortnight. When I got there I had a heart attack and saw the resident physician. He told me I was too fat and fat was pressing on my heart and if I did not do something about it I was liable to drop down dead at any moment. In fact I was walking on the edge of a precipice. He undertook to cure me, the cure being a complete fast. Being thoroughly frightened by his diagnoses I went through the treatment, rigorous though it was, and fasted for 50 days and 50 nights. For the first two weeks I had a few ounces daily of raw carrot and mustard and cress. This brought on acute sickness and indigestion and had to be stopped and for a fortnight I lived on nothing but water. For the rest of the fast I was allowed twelve grapes daily. At the end of this time I had lost three stone in weight, dropping from 11st. 10lbs. to 8st. 7lbs. When I finished the treatment some people told me I looked dreadful—'An emaciated

30 'Mephy' Robertson committed suicide on Friday 14 June 1940 and the news reached Baird on 18 June. He attended the funeral in Ryde on the following day.*

31 Baird entered Tempsford Hall near Sandy, in Bedfordshire, on 13 May 1941. On 21 May he suffered a coronary thrombosis and he stayed at the Hall until early September.*

scarecrow', others, that I looked 100% better; whatever my appearance may have been, I certainly felt very much better.

While this fast was going on I did not stay in bed but wandered about the grounds of the hotel and there made many pleasant friends, among them Mr. Philip Morrell[32] who urged me to write my autobiography. The idea of writing a book had been in my mind for many years and I had prepared a number of notes. While the cure was progressing I commenced to put the project into practice. I had a typist to call at the hotel and it was there that the first chapter of Sermons, Socks and Television was dictated.[33]

32 Philip Morrell (1870–1943) had been a successful barrister and Liberal member of parliament, but he had left politics during World War I on pacifist grounds. He was the husband of Lady Ottoline Morrell, an aristocratic literary hostess who presided over gatherings of intellectuals (the Bloomsbury Group) in the 1920s and 1930s.*

33 Among other possible titles for his memoirs, Baird had jotted down 'Television and Myself'. The present title is based on that idea with a more direct style.

Chapter Ten

written by Margaret Cecilia Baird in 1948

John Logie Baird, my dear husband, did not live to see his autobiography published; since his untimely death many requests have been made for its publication and I am venturing to add a last chapter.

At the time that he ceased writing, the war was still to drag on for 3 more years—years for him of heartbreak and anxiety. He met each difficulty with his usual patience and tolerance and the acceptance which his early religious training had instilled into him. His work continued at his private laboratory with a staff drastically curtailed, but nevertheless a handful of faithful and adoring men who toiled through the black-outs, air raids, shortages, interminable delays for apparatus ordered, and in 1944 the near miss of a flying bomb which partially wrecked the house but miraculously left all the apparatus undamaged.

Much new work was brilliantly done to improve colour television and television in stereoscopic relief.[1] His savings were all thrown into these war years during which he pursued, with dogged faith, his dream of being in the forefront when peace came and television would resume its place as a new and widespread industry. He often told me that if it had not been for his appointment with Cable and Wireless as Technical Adviser, he could not have kept going. Apart from the financial aspect, courage and confidence in himself were stimulated by the courteous and dignified welcome he always received at Electra House. His gratitude and affection for Sir Edward Wilshaw[2] were deep.

During the summer months he kept going, enjoying reasonable health, but each winter was taken ill, the attacks becoming more pronounced each succeeding year.

With a consideration that was characteristic of him it was his wish that I kept our two children in Cornwall, where we evacuated at the outbreak of war, and each time he could manage to be with us at Bude he said 'what a

1 Baird's pioneering work in this area led to what is now known as '4D imaging'.

2 Sir Edward Wilshaw (1879–1968) was the Chairman of Cable and Wireless. Baird's project was to develop a system for rapid transmission of images ('fast facsimile'). Results were announced to the press in the summer of 1944.*

Baird at work in his laboratory during the war. (Hastings Museum and Art Gallery)

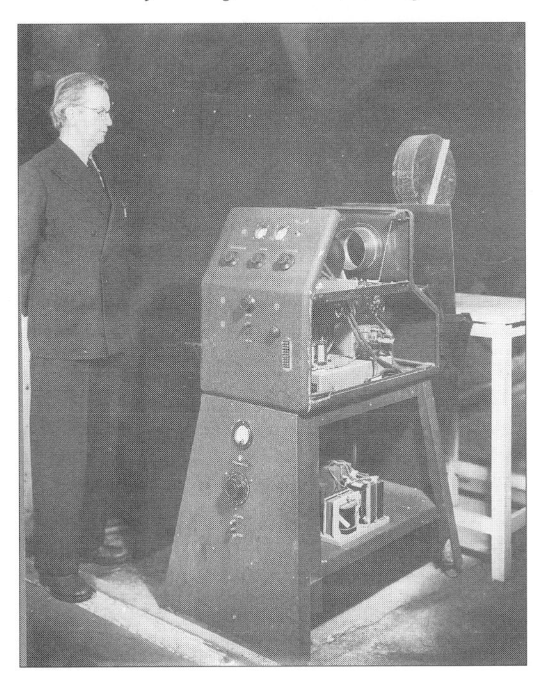

Baird with his 'fast facsimile' equipment developed for Cable and Wireless, probably in 1944. (Hastings Museum and Art Gallery).

Diana and Malcolm on the beach at Bude, '...what a paradise for the children'.

paradise for the children—some good is coming out of all this evil'. Much of his work was thought out whilst taking long slow walks over the downs, notebook in hand, and I took down many of his patents in long hand at his dictation. He was particularly happy in the fine weather and his kindly humorous manner made him many friends.

Towards the end of 1944[3] I was staying in London with him when he had one of his strange attacks, followed by a feverish state which lasted about a week. His doctor advised me to take him out of London to Crowborough—so we left the air raids and stayed for a time in that invigorating air. At this time one of his most ardent wishes was just coming to fruition, namely the formation of a small private company to put up enough capital to continue the development of his inventions. He had tried this group and that, but no one was risking any money on television when the war looked like lasting for

3 Entries from my parents' diaries indicate that Baird became ill in late 1943; he stayed at Crowborough until 14 March, 1944.*

ever. Finally his own Helensburgh friend of his youth, that famous star Jack Buchanan, showed his faith in the work and, after several months of discussion and negotiation, a small company was formed and new premises were taken in the West End of London.[4]

It is impossible for me to attempt to finish this book in anything resembling the manner in which Logie[5] himself would have achieved, because these last two years for me were years of acute sadness and anxiety as I watched his health deteriorating. Doctor after doctor was consulted, specialists examined X-ray photographs and cardiograms and gave opinions—all agreed that rest was essential but none foresaw or hinted at the tragedy that was soon to overtake us. Rest was the one thing that he could not and would not do. I think that inaction for him would have been death in life. His mind was ever active and the misleading factor was the fascination of his conversation, especially with men of intellect. A doctor might begin by treating him as a patient, but in a few minutes the professional atmosphere would disappear, Logie's eyes would twinkle, and brilliant talk would ensue, irrelevant to his illness but full of wit and humour. Every doctor who saw him must have thought, 'here is a genius undoubtedly, highly strung, but a mortally sick man, no.'

His powers of recuperation were tremendous, especially if he could get into warmth. He dreamed of going abroad into what he called 'bursting, bubbling sunshine'. He said to me once, 'my days are numbered; I have shot my bolt; I expect this feeling of general malaise must be age creeping on, yet I do not *feel* old, any older than I did when I was 25.'

As 1945 proceeded, he was happier about this new company than I have ever seen him. In his opinion all its members were trustworthy, refined and altogether a more responsible team than he had had about him before the war. Another happy day was when Mr. Seeman[6] of Capital and Provincial News Theatres came to see us, quite out of the blue, and showed a respect for Logie and an enthusiasm for television that was most cheering. Logie became a member of their Board and Mr. Seeman gave him facilities in a news theatre in the heart of London for experiments with big screen work.

One day in November 1945 we took the two children to London for a treat, and he was proud to show us all over the new premises where all the apparatus was gradually being installed. Unfortunately there was no lift in this

4 The company was called John Logie Baird Ltd., with offices at 4 Upper Grosvenor Street. It produced television sets for the post-war market and in 1948 it merged with Scophony Ltd. to form Scophony-Baird Ltd. Later, the Baird brand-name was taken over by Radio Rentals Ltd.*

5 My mother called my father Logie in preference to John, a name she disliked.

6 Samuel Seeman became Managing Director of Scophony Ltd. in 1947 shortly before it merged with John Logie Baird Ltd.*

The Telechrome, demonstrated in 1944, was the world's first cathode ray tube for showing colour television. It was Baird's last invention. (Royal Television Society)

4 story building and I have a painful memory of his slow ascent by the staircase, pausing and gasping at each step, but joking to us that he would 'join us in a quarter of an hour'. His weakness was increasing apace now, but few people could have realised it, so brave and indomitable a show did he put up.

By now we had taken a small house in Bexhill[7] to be nearer his work. The war was over, but travelling was still uncomfortable. Our own house at Sydenham was too damaged to occupy and it was still impossible to get repairs done. He liked the sea air and spent as much time as he could spare with us.

Christmas 1945 was exceptionally mild, and he was with us for a fortnight, in quite good health I thought. He returned to London on Jan.1st and after a few days caught a bad chill. It was not until a month later that I brought him back to Bexhill and the blow fell.[8] I am not going to dwell on the next thirteen weeks when he lay fighting for his life, helped by day and night nurses, doctors and specialists. To everyone's surprise he actually seemed to make a miraculous recovery. I knew that an active life would be out of the question for him, and was preparing for his retirement in some warm place abroad. He made notes of his future plans up to the day before he died. He in his visionary mind could see vast possibilities and opportunities and he said how cruel a fate it was to be stricken in body and be clear in mind. But God in his mercy did not let him live to be tortured with the restrictions of an invalid's existence, and released his lovable ardent spirit so gently that he did not stir in his sleep.[9]

He had fought a valiant battle all his life, and much that he had prophesied may not come to pass in our lifetimes, but his dream of television telecommunications is all quite practicable for a future age. His expectation that televised events will be seen on big screens (not necessarily in cinemas) will also be realised. His stereoscopic images, working so realistically in his laboratory 3 years ago, will be commonplace. Few can work with the speed of John Logie Baird who brought forward a new industry and in the space of 22 years produced work that will prove an inspiration for many minds and hands for countless years to come.

He felt keenly the lack of recognition but time will show the quality of his work and how much he has added to human knowledge and achievement. A true gentleman and a great man has passed from us.

7 The house, now known as Baird Court, was directly across the road from the railway station.

8 Baird had a stroke on 2 February 1946.

9 John Logie Baird died on 14 June 1946 and the funeral took place in Helensburgh on 17 June.

Further Reading—Recent Books

Antony Kamm and Malcolm Baird, *John Logie Baird: A Life*, National Museum of Scotland (2002)

A complete biography including technical, business and personal aspects; it has been the source of information for many of the footnotes in this edition of the memoirs.

Donald F. McLean, *Restoring Baird's Image*, Institution of Electrical Engineers (2000)

On the computer-aided restoration of disc recordings of early television.

Russell Burns, *John Logie Baird, Television Pioneer*, Institution of Electrical Engineers (2000)

An essentially technical book which includes a list of Baird's 177 patents.

Ray Herbert, *Seeing by Wireless—The Story of Baird Television*, PW Publishing, Broadstone BH18 8PW (1997)

A short account including many historic photographs of Baird's work, in particular his colour and stereoscopic television during World War II.

Index